Staying Healthy God's Way

Unlocking God's Power for Health, Happiness, and Prosperity

Dr. John J. Skorusa Jr.

Staying Healthy God's Way
by Dr. John J. Skorusa Jr.

Printed in the United States of America

Library of Congress Control Number: 2002106159
ISBN 1-591600-89-8

Xulon Press
11350 Random Hills Road
Suite 800
Fairfax, VA 22030
(703) 279-6511
XulonPress.com

To order additional copies, call 1-866-909-BOOK (2665).

To Dan & Marlene Stewart,
May God Bless you
with abundant health!
John Skousen

This book is dedicated to God almighty, whose love and guidance made this work possible. Praise God for the wisdom, discernment, and perseverance to complete this book for the health, happiness, and prosperity of His people.

Special thanks to my family, Diana, Jennifer, and Daniel for their support and encouragement that allowed me to share God's message with the world.

Table of Contents

Page

List of Figures and Tables

Figures

Tables

Introduction

The health of a person can be indicative of several parameters such as how a person feels, what a person thinks, what a person does, their moral values, character, and attitude. Likewise, the health of a nation is characterized by the cumulative health of its people. As a consensus, how do the people feel, what do the people think, what do the people do, and what are the moral values, character, and attitudes of the people.

My purpose for writing this book is to make you think about your health and the health of the United States of America. I want to educate you about basic health concepts that aren't taught in school or handed down from generation to generation. I want to motivate you to take action and change your ways for the betterment of yourself, your family, and your nation. And finally, I want to encourage you that there is always hope. No matter what your circumstances, there is always hope if you rely on God.

The following scripture from the Book of Ezekiel will help explain my desire and motive for writing this book.

> Once again a message came to me from the LORD:
> "Son of man, give your people this message: When I bring an army against a country, the people of that land choose a watchman.
> When the watchman sees the enemy coming, he blows the alarm to warn the people.
> Then if those who hear the alarm refuse to take action – well, it is their own fault if they die.
> They heard the warning but wouldn't listen, so the responsibility is theirs. If they had listened to the warning, they could have saved their lives.
> But if the watchman sees the enemy coming and doesn't sound the alarm to warn the people, he is responsible for their deaths. They will die in their sins, but I will hold the watchman accountable.

"Now, son of man, I am making you a watchman for the people of Israel. Therefore, listen to what I say and warn them for me.
Ezekiel 33:1-7 (New Living Translation)

God has called upon me to deliver a message to His people. The message is clear, God is concerned about His people of this world. He is especially concerned about the people of the United States. For the United States is a world leader and provides great influence over the rest of the nations of the world. America, once the model of western civilization, is faltering. America has a cancer growing and it is eating away at the basic structures of American society.

If a country can only be as strong as its people, it's no wonder why America is faltering. Americans are sick. Americans are sick because they have strayed from God's principles and divine guidance. Americans are sick in body, mind, and spirit and God is concerned. God is concerned because a nation of people that He built into one of the greatest empires in the history of mankind has turned their back on Him.

God sent this same warning out to the people of Israel several thousand years ago and they failed to listen and obey. Israel was destroyed. God is now sending this same message out to the people of America. Will we learn from history and correct our mistakes or will we suffer the same consequences as Israel?

It is indeed an honor and privilege to bring you this message from God. His message is clear, repent, change your ways, turn back to God and He will restore this nation and its people. Failure to hear and obey this message will lead to destruction and disaster. It's not too late to revitalize and restore America to greatness if we follow God.

As God's messenger, I've given you His message. As the watchman, I'm blowing the alarm to warn you that it is time to take action, now! It's time to take action before America totally self-destructs in a mire of immorality, corruption, hatred, and apathy.

The revitalization of America starts with you. Each American needs to take personal responsibility for returning America to greatness. A nation is only as good as its people. Each one of you must start by taking action to remove the sickness from your body, mind, and spirit and help others to do the same. God will return America to a happy, healthy and prosperous nation if you will turn to Him.

Pleasure and pain are two strong motivating human emotions. I pray that the pleasure of knowing God's love and will for your life will motivate you to read this book. I also pray that the pain and suffering experienced from your disobedience and not living up to God's expectations will encourage you to put the principles of this book into action. There is always hope if you follow God's way!

Section I - Overview of Health

CHAPTER 1

What is Health?

What does the word health mean to you? This is an elusive question. Different people have different ideas about the meaning of health. For some people it means never getting sick. For some people it means being vibrant and having abundant energy. For some people it means being able to do any activity they choose to do. For others it might mean living to 100 years of age without debilitating pain.

The dictionary definition of health is "the state of being free from physical disease or pain." Is this an accurate definition of health? There are some people who do not have any diagnosed disease or pain, but they do not feel good. They do not enjoy life. They lack energy, vigor and motivation and have a difficult time making it through the day. I do not consider a person in this condition to be healthy even though they meet this definition of health.

On the other hand, let us consider a person who is defined as healthy - free of disease and pain, and is robust, energetic, and very athletic. This person is a weekend sports enthusiast. One weekend this person plays in a softball tournament. Come Monday morning this person is in pain with sore, stiff, overworked muscles. Because of the muscle pain, this person no longer meets the definition of being healthy. Would you say that this person is unhealthy? Absolutely not!

No, "the state of being free from physical disease or pain" is not an accurate or complete definition of health. There is more to a healthy state than just being disease and pain free. Health also includes feeling good, and having the energy and ability to do the things you want to do.

The health of an individual is also very subjective. There is good health, poor health and health somewhere in between. Our health changes over time. Nobody has superior health all the time.

Therefore, we are always challenged to maintain and improve our health. Your health is based on what you make of it.

We are creatures composed of three entities: body, mind and spirit. Our overall health is directly related to the refinement of each entity according to God's specifications. With respect to the body, I'm talking about nourishment, exercise and rest. God created man and women with specific physical needs. To what degree we satisfy these needs directly impacts our physical health. With respect to the mind, I'm talking about attitude, knowledge, character and discipline. God, through his biblical word, gives us direction about proper attitude and mental strength and focus. Consequently, the state of our mind also affects our health. With respect to the spirit, I'm talking about the Holy Spirit of God. Knowing the Holy Spirit brings us a Godly perspective, eternal life, a purpose for our earthly life, hope and a reason for having faith in God. The degree to which we acknowledge and follow the Holy Spirit also impacts our health.

Synergism is the concept that individual entities working together create a greater total effect than each entity working alone. The body, mind and spirit working together create a greater impact on good health than the body, mind or spirit working alone. This is a crucial concept to remember. Good health relies on a balance of body, mind and spirit working together pursuing God's will for our life.

For illustration purposes, I will use diagrams to reflect different stages of health. Each circle represents one of the human entities, body, mind and spirit. The black dot in the center of the diagram represents optimum achievement. The degree to which these circles reach optimum achievement and overlap each other depicts our current state of health.

Figure 1-1 depicts perfect health, the perfection or total unison of body, mind and spirit. Unfortunately for us, only one person has ever achieved this state and that was Jesus Christ. Only Jesus was perfect in body, mind and spirit and achieved perfect health.

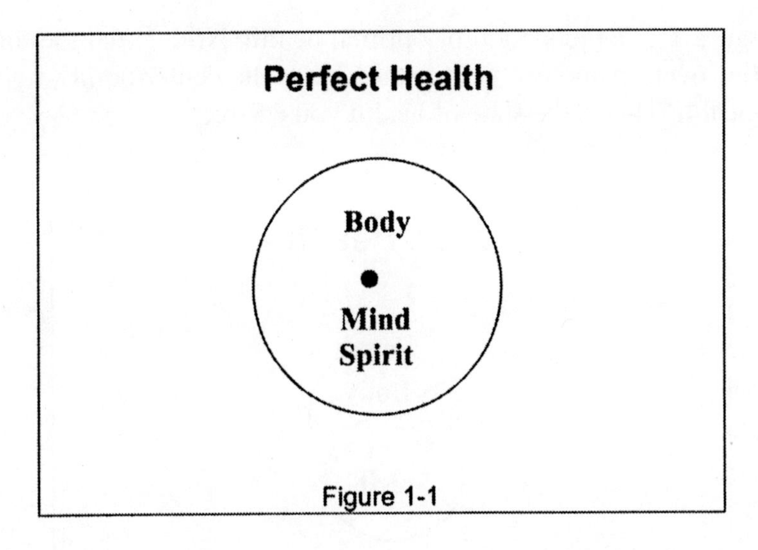

Figure 1-1

Figure 1-2 depicts poor health. This condition is the opposite of perfect health. Notice that there is no overlap between any of the entities and each entity is far away from the center point of optimal health. A person in this state of health will usually exhibit chronic illnesses of the body, mind and spirit. Chronic illnesses such as obesity, cardiovascular disease, cancer, diabetes, pulmonary embolism, digestive disorders, arthritis, hormonal imbalances, negative attitude, depression, loneliness, insecurity and low self-worth just to mention a few.

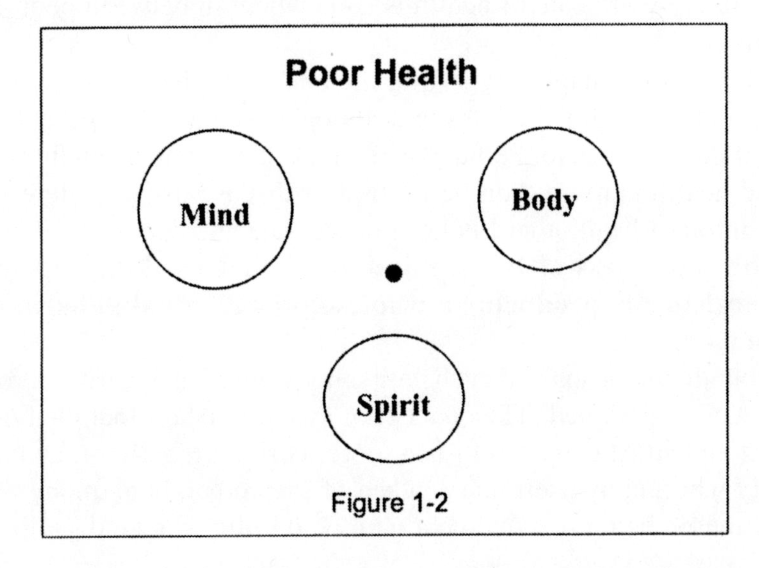

Figure 1-2

Figure 1-3 depicts good or optimal health. Notice that the three entities overlap and each entity surrounds the center point of optimal health. This is the state of health you desire.

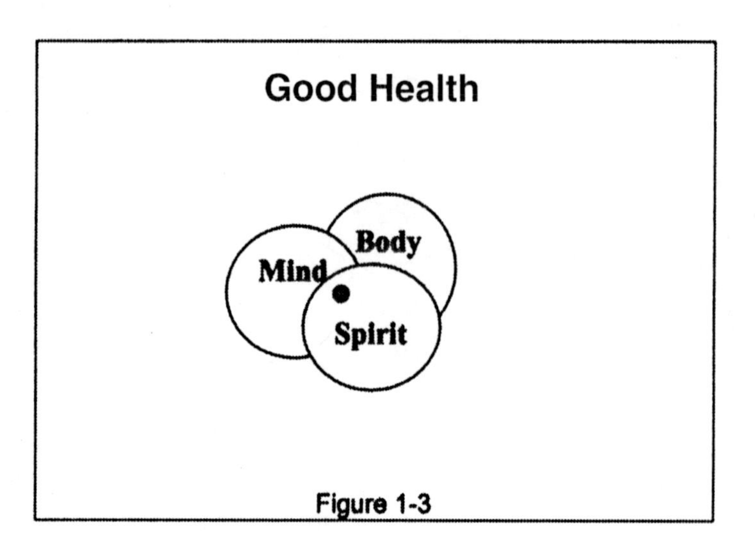

Figure 1-3

Take a moment and access your current state of health. Draw a circle diagram like the ones above to depict your current health. What does it look like? You may be thinking to yourself that I've not yet arrived at the model of good or optimal health but I'm not exactly falling apart as the model of poor health depicts. More than likely your state of health is somewhere in between poor and optimal.

I began this chapter by asking the question what does the word health mean to you? Perhaps your thoughts about health have taken on a new perspective. Perhaps you have a better understanding that good health is more than being free of disease or pain. Here is a definition of health that I believe is accurate and complete. **Health is the soundness of body, mind and spirit working together synergistically producing a wholesome individual in harmony with God.**

Soundness means that each entity, body, mind and spirit is strong and well maintained. The concept of synergy means that the body, mind and spirit can accomplish more working together than each entity working by itself independent of each other. In harmony with God means being in agreement with God, following God's will for your life. Putting all this together, here is another way to rephrase this definition of health. **Health is the result of a strong body, mind and spirit working together to produce a complete individual that follows the will of God.**

Maybe you are not a healthy individual. No matter what your current health condition, I want to encourage you that there is hope. There is a way to improve and maintain your health – God's way!

> Pay attention, my child, to what I say. Listen carefully. Don't lose sight of my words. Let them penetrate deep within your heart, for they bring life and radiant health to anyone who discovers their meaning.
> **Proverbs 4:20-22 (The New Living Translation)**

CHAPTER 2

Are Americans Healthy?

Keeping in mind that health is the soundness of body, mind and spirit working together, let us review some health related statistics. Then you decide, are Americans healthy?

Americans spend more money on health care than any other nation in the world. Over one trillion dollars will be spent on health care for Americans this year. Annual health care expenditures are expected to continue to grow by roughly 100 million dollars per year. American health care expenditures are expected to reach two trillion dollars by the year 2007.

The United States spends a tremendous amount of money on health care and has the most advanced high-tech health care system in the world. Yet we rank 23rd in longevity (see Table 2-1).

Did you know that cardiovascular disease, disease of the heart and blood vessels, claimed 949,619 lives in the United States in 1998? According to the American Heart Association, more than 2,600 Americans die each day of cardiovascular disease – an average of 1 death every 33 seconds. Today it is estimated that 60 million Americans have one or more types of cardiovascular disease. The American Heart Association estimates the cost of cardiovascular disease in the United States in 2001 at 298 billion dollars.

This year approximately 553,400 Americans will die of cancer. According to the American Cancer Society more than 1,500 Americans die each day of cancer – an average of 1 death every minute. In the year 2001, about 1.2 million new cancer cases will be diagnosed. The financial costs of cancer is great both to the individual and to society as a whole. The National Institutes of Health estimates overall annual costs for cancer at 180 billion dollars.

More than 51 million Americans are estimated to have a mental disorder. This includes more than 40 million American adults affected by one or more mental disorders. Mental illness also affects our children. It is estimated that approximately 12 million youth have severe emotional or behavioral problems that significantly interfere with their daily functioning. On a national level, mental illness costs are estimated to be more than $150 billion annually for treatment, costs of social service and disability payments, lost productivity, and premature mortality.

The World Health Report 1999
(The World Health Organization)

Rank	Country	Population (000)	Average Life Expectancy	Health Expenditures (% of GDP)
1	Japan	126 281	79.9	7.2
2	Iceland	276	79.1	8.0
3	Canada	30 563	79.0	9.2
4	Switzerland	7 299	78.6	9.8
5	Sweden	8 875	78.5	7.3
6	Australia	18 520	78.3	8.6
7	Norway	4 419	78.2	7.9
8	France	58 683	78.1	9.7
9	Greece	10 600	78.1	5.9
10	Italy	57 369	78.1	7.6
11	Spain	39 628	78.0	7.7
12	Netherlands	15 678	77.9	8.6
13	Cyprus	771	77.8	4.6
14	Israel	5 984	77.7	4.1
15	Belgium	10 141	77.2	7.9
16	United Kingdom	58 649	77.2	6.9
17	Singapore	3 476	77.1	3.5
18	Malta	384	77.1	7.4
19	Germany	82 133	77.1	10.5
20	Austria	8 140	76.9	8.0
21	New Zealand	3 796	76.9	7.2
22	Finland	5 154	76.8	7.5
23	United States of America	274 028	76.7	14.0

Table 2-1

Suicide claims more lives than homicide each year. In 1999, suicide claimed 29,199 lives. On the average, 80 people kill themselves each day. That is one successful suicide every 18 minutes. It is estimated that there are 730,000 suicide attempts each year.

Fifty percent of couples who marry for the first time will be divorced in 10 years. Sixty percent of all second marriages end in divorce. Over 1 Million children *each year* experience their parents' divorce.

- 25% of those children will be high school drop-outs.
- 40% will receive psychological help.
- 65% never build a good post divorce relationship with their fathers.
- 30% never build a good post divorce relationship with their mothers.

Compared to people who have grown up with both parents in the home, adult children of divorce are 59% more likely to have problems in their own marriage.

Approximately 1 million teens in the United States become pregnant each year.

There are approximately 1.4 million abortions performed in the United States each year. That equates to 3,835 abortions every day and 1 abortion every 23 seconds. The overwhelming majority of all abortions are performed as a means of birth control.

Nearly 14 million Americans are alcoholics or have significant problems due to their use of alcohol. There are more than 6 million children trapped in homes with an untreated alcoholic — homes in which they are often physically, sexually or emotionally abused. Alcohol contributes to the death of more than 100,000 people every year. More than 10,000 babies are born every year with intellectual disabilities associated with fetal alcohol syndrome. Annual costs for treatment of alcohol-related medical problems are estimated at 166 billion dollars.

The following crime statistics for 2000 are provided by the Federal Bureau of Investigation. Each number represents the annual total number of offenses reported:

- Murder 11,606
- Forcible Rape 92,846
- Robbery 406,201
- Aggravated Assault 905,249
- Burglary 2,054,218
- Larceny-Theft 6,963,451

The following crime clock represents the frequency of occurrence of these crimes.

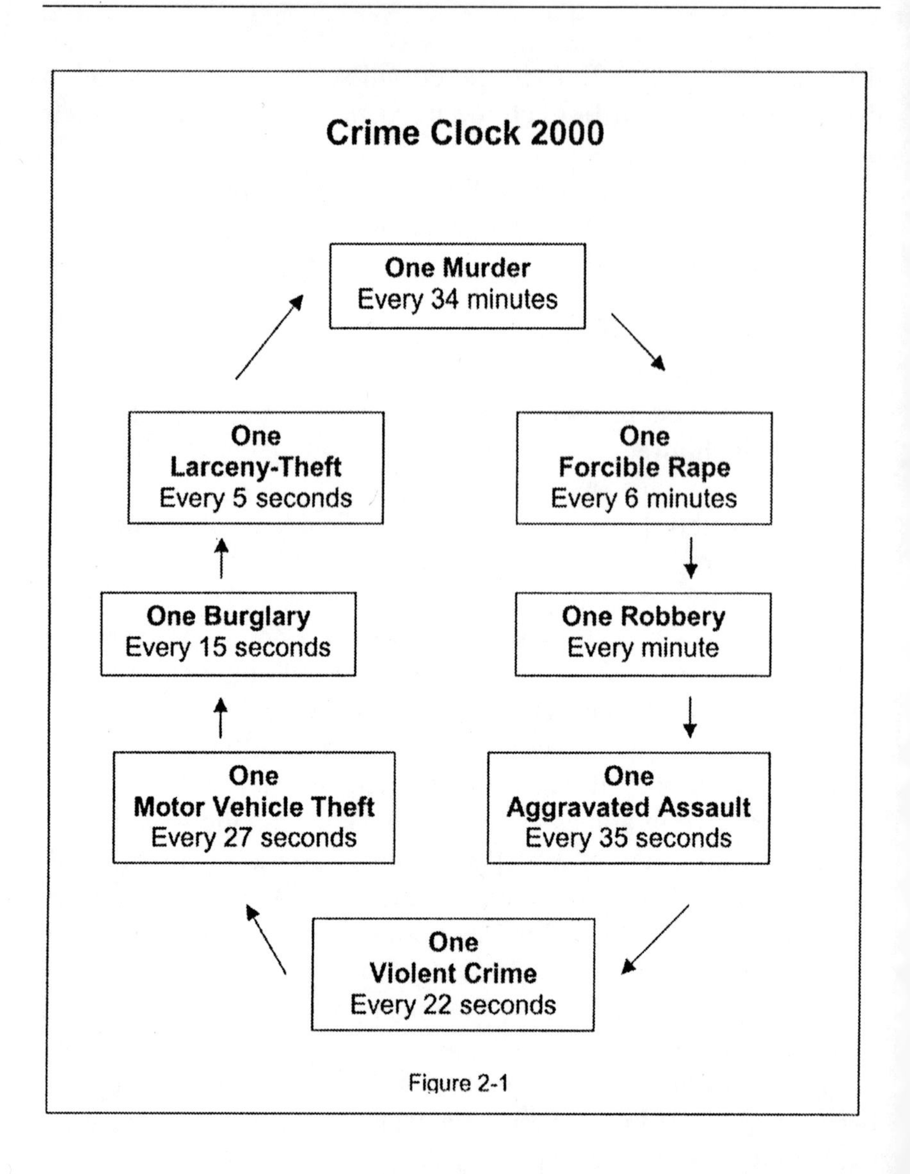

Figure 2-1

Many consider the United States the most powerful, affluent nation in the world. America is known as the land of opportunity with abundant jobs, technology, housing, food and education. Yet of all the industrialized nations we are one the most unhealthy countries in the world. America suffers from the typical ills of a rich, affluent, powerful nation: arrogance, decrepit thinking, impoverished morality, and misplaced values. A nation whose leading causes of death are heart disease, cancer, and stroke (see Table 2-2), totally preventable diseases, is truly sick in body. A nation that allows infant genocide, the intentional killing of 1.4 million babies per year, is truly sick in mind. And finally, a prideful nation who turns their back on God and becomes self-reliant, is truly sick in spirit.

10 Leading Causes of Death in the United States
(Center for Disease Control and Prevention)

1. Heart Disease
2. Cancer
3. Stroke
4. Lung Disease
5. Accidents
6. Pneumonia & Influenza
7. Diabetes
8. Suicide
9. Kidney Disease
10. Liver Disease

Table 2-2

As the aforementioned statistics demonstrate, it is quite evident that Americans are not healthy. Many of us suffer from an enormous amount of pain, misery, and disease. Are you hurting right now? Do you suffer from fatigue, loneliness, or depression? Do you have purpose in your life? Do you jump out of bed in the morning, full of vigor and excited about the challenges of the day ahead of you? If not, do not despair, there is hope. There is a way we can all have joy, health, and prosperity – God's way!

> Don't be afraid, for I am with you. Do not be dismayed, for I am your God.
> I will strengthen you. I will help you. I will uphold you with my victorious right hand.
> **Isaiah 41:10 (The New Living Translation)**

> Don't worry about anything; instead, pray about everything. Tell God what you need, and thank him for all he has done.

If you do this, you will experience God's peace, which is far more wonderful than the human mind can understand. His peace will guard your hearts and minds as you live in Christ Jesus.
Philippians 4:6-7 (The New Living Translation)

CHAPTER 3

Biblical Perspective of Health

Historical Longevity

The longevity of our early patriarchs of the Bible lasted for nearly a millennium. Adam, the first man created by God, lived for 930 years. The longest living man was Methuselah who lived to a ripe old age of 969 years. This extraordinary longevity lasted for ten generations. Noah was the last man to live over 900 years of age. He lived for 950 years.

How could people live over 900 years? Well, from our current perspective, it seems impossible. The Bible gives us no specific explanation of what the conditions on earth were like in those days. Speculation has it that the earth's atmospheric condition was considerably different than it is today to support life for such an extensive period of time. For instance, the oxygen content of the air was probably much higher than our current 20 percent oxygen content of today. The earth was also probably more fertile than it is today providing excellent nourishment.

Why do people no longer have 900-year lifespans? Over the first ten generations of man, God grew tired of their wickedness and disobedience. God decided to reduce the lifespan of man to 120 years.

> Then the Lord said, " My Spirit will not contend with man forever, for he is mortal, his days will be a hundred and twenty years."
> **Genesis 6:3 (New International Version, NIV)**

God was grieved over the sinful ways of man. He was sorry that he ever created man and decided to eradicate all living creatures from the earth, including man.

> The Lord saw how great man's wickedness on the earth had become, and that every inclination of the thoughts of his heart was only evil all the time. The Lord was grieved that he had made man on the earth, and his heart was filled with pain. So the Lord said, "I will wipe mankind, whom I have created, from the face of the earth – men and animals, and creatures that move along the ground, and birds of the air – for I am grieved that I have made them."
> **Genesis 6:5-7 (New International Version, NIV)**

Noah was a righteous man, blameless among the people of his time, and he walked with God. Noah and his family were chosen by God to perpetuate the human species and creatures of the earth. God directed Noah to build a large ark and then gather the creatures and his family aboard the ark. God then sent the great flood and destroyed all mankind from the face of the earth – man, animals and all creatures.

After the great floodwaters receded, God blessed Noah and his family and gave them the task of being fruitful, multiplying and repopulating the earth. Noah and his family were truly blessed and did an extraordinary job repopulating the world. Today we have over six billion people living on the earth. However, after the great flood lifespans began to spiral downward. Noah lived 950 years, but his son Shem only lived 600 years. Several generations later Abraham lived 175 years, Issac lived 180 years, Jacob lived 147 years, and Moses lived 120 years (see Table 3-1).

Current Human Longevity

How long do you expect to live? I hope you answered 120 years. God revealed to us in Genesis 6:3 that man shall live 120 years. There are some cultures around the world where people routinely live to 120 years of age, but not in industrialized nations like the United States. The average expected longevity of Americans is 76.7 years. Environmental pollution, malnutrition and a stressful lifestyle has taken its toll on the longevity and quality of life of Americans.

God's overall plan is that man shall live 120 years. Of course, not everybody enjoys this longevity. People often die at a much earlier age. Some due to God's will and some due to self-abuse and devastating lifestyles. It is God's command that you plan and live a lifestyle pleasing to him. God wants you to live a lifestyle that will allow you to be happy, healthy and prosperous to an age of 120 years. Anything less than this is disobedient and displeasing to God.

There are at least five cultures known for their health and longevity. They are the Hunza in the Karakoram Mountains in Northern Pakistan, the Vilcabamba in the Andean Mountains in Ecuador, the Titicaca in the Andean Mountains in Peru, the Russian Georgians in the Caucasus Mountains, and the Tibetans in the Himalayan Mountains in China. Some common denominators of these five cultures include:

- The communities are found at elevations of 8,500 feet or greater
- The annual precipitation is less than 2 inches
- Their water source for drinking and irrigation comes from glacial melt
- There is no heavy industry to pollute air, water or food
- Only natural fertilizer is used
- Western allopathic medicine is not available.

God really does allow some of us to reach the age of 120 years. According to the Guinness book of world records, the oldest living man was Shigechiyo Izumi of Japan. He lived 120 years (1865 – 1986). The oldest living woman was Jeanne Calment of France. She lived 122 years (1875 – 1997).

Biblical Genealogical Longevity

Adam (930 years of age)
Seth (912)
Enosh (905)
Kenan (910)
Mahalalel (895)
Jared (962)
Enoch (365)
Methuselah (969)
Lamech (777)
Noah [950 – (2948-1998 BC)] **Time of the Great Flood**
Shem (600)
Arphaxad (437)
Shelah (433)
Eber (464)
Peleg (239)
Reu (239)
Serug (230)
Nahor (148)
Terah (205)
Abraham (175) [Sarah (127)]
Issac (180) Ishmael (137)
Jacob (147)
Judah Levi (137) Joseph (110)
| Kohath (133)
| Amran (137)
| (9 Generations) Moses [120 – (1571-1451 BC)]
|
|
David [70 – (1085-1015 BC)]
Solomon [60 – (1035-975 BC)]

Table 3-1

God's Desire for Our Health and Prosperity

In order to understand God's desire for our health and prosperity, we need to start at the beginning and look at the big picture. Who is God and what does he expect of us? The first few chapters of the book of Genesis tell us that God is the creator of the universe. He created the heavens and the earth. He created the sun and the moon. He created the mountains and the oceans. He created every living creature and plant and of course, he created you and me!

The earth is the Lord's, and everything in it, the world, and all who live in it.
Psalms 24:1 (New International Version, NIV)

The highest heavens belong to the Lord, but the earth he has given to man.
Psalms 115:16 (New International Version, NIV)

God created man to be rulers and caretakers of all that he created on earth. God owns the earth, but he has entrusted us to care for it. God expects us to take an active role in caring for His creation. This includes taking care of the earth, animals, plants, ourselves, and each other. You must remember that you are responsible to God for how you use the earth and everything on it. You are to manage according to His standards and purpose, not yours. Daily tasks such as managing your time and money, taking care of your health, your family, your employer, and caring for our environment is to be done for the glory of God.

God tells us through His word that he has a plan for your life and He will bless you if you are obedient, follow His commands and do what is right. God wants you to be happy, healthy and prosperous. God will show you the way to achieve happiness, health and prosperity. All you have to do is follow His plan.

For I know the plans I have for you, "declares the Lord," plans to prosper you and not to harm you, plans to give you hope and a future.
Jeremiah 29:11 (New International Version, NIV)

I will never forget your commandments, for you have used them to restore my joy and health.
Psalms 119:93 (The New Living Translation)

Happy are those who obey his decrees and search for him with all their hearts.
Psalms 119:2 (The New Living Translation)

"If you keep my laws and are careful to obey my commands, I will send the seasonal rains. The land will

> then yield its crops, and the trees will produce their fruit. You will eat your fill and live securely in your land. "I will give you peace in the land, and you will be able to sleep without fear. I will remove the wild animals from your land and protect you from your enemies.
> **Leviticus 26:3-6 (The New Living Translation)**

What happens if I refuse to follow God's way? Failure to follow God's commands and to do what is right in God's mind leads to sickness, pain, death and eternal separation from God.

> "If you will listen carefully to the voice of the LORD your God and do what is right in his sight, obeying his commands and laws, then I will not make you suffer the diseases I sent on the Egyptians; for I am the LORD who heals you."
> **Exodus 15:26 (The New Living Translation)**

> "If you refuse to obey all the terms of this law that are written in this book, and if you do not fear the glorious and awesome name of the LORD your God, then the LORD will overwhelm both you and your children with indescribable plagues. These plagues will be intense and without relief, making you miserable and unbearably sick. He will bring against you all the diseases of Egypt that you feared so much, and they will claim you.
> **Deuteronomy 28:58-61 (The New Living Translation)**

> "Not everyone who says to me, 'Lord, Lord,' will enter the kingdom of heaven, but only he who does the will of my Father who is in heaven."
> **Matthew 7:21 (New International Version, NIV)**

It is God's desire for you to live a long, healthy, fulfilling life. God wants to share His peace and joy with you. He wants to bless you beyond your wildest imagination. Will you accept His wonderful gifts? All you have to do is obey his commands and laws and do what is right in His sight. Will you surrender your pride and live the life God has planned for you?

You cannot be truly healthy in body, mind and spirit without God. He is the 'Great Physician' and knows exactly what you need to live an abundant life. If your health is not what you want it to be, I suggest changing your direction. Turn away from your disobedience and worldly living and turn to God. Change your ways now, before it's too late! Everyone can improve his or her health following God's way. There is hope because God always keeps His promise.

> . . . . The LORD is faithful to all his promises and loving toward all he has made.
> **Psalms 145:13 (New International Version, NIV)**

> He is the one who made heaven and earth, the sea, and everything in them. He is the one who keeps every promise forever,
> **Psalms 146:6 (The New Living Translation)**

> So God has given us both his promise and his oath. These two things are unchangeable because it is impossible for God to lie. Therefore, we who have fled to him for refuge can take new courage, for we can hold on to his promise with confidence.
> **Hebrews 6:8 (The New Living Translation)**

CHAPTER 4

Why Do People Get Sick?

Have you ever wondered why some people seem to be healthy most of the time while others seem to be sickly? Still others have permanent afflictions that will last a lifetime. If God truly wants us to live long, happy, healthy and prosperous lives, why is there so much sickness?

Biblical Reasons for Sickness

From a biblical perspective, there are two reasons why people get sick. The first reason people get sick is for the glory of God and the second reason people get sick is because of sin.

Sometimes God uses sickness and physical afflictions for His glory. He uses sickness to teach us lessons of life, build character, to draw us closer to Him, or for whatever reason that He may choose. Sickness in this category is difficult for us to understand because it often occurs for no apparent reason. God has a plan for each of us and sometimes His plan includes sickness or physical disabilities. A common biblical example of God using sickness for His glory is found in the Gospel of John, Chapter 9. This is the story of a man who was blind from birth.

> As he went along, he saw a man blind from birth. His disciples asked him, "Rabbi, who sinned, this man or his parents, that he was born blind?" "Neither this man nor his parents sinned," said Jesus, "but this happened so that the work of God might be displayed in his life.
> **John 9:1-3 (New International Version, NIV)**

This man was born blind for a purpose. So that Jesus could restore his sight and show the world God's love and power of healing.

Although God does use sickness for His glory, the overwhelming amount of sickness in the world is a product of sin. What is sin? Simply put, sin is the rebellious act of disobeying God. Some examples of sin are adultery, fornication, idolatry, murder, drunkenness, jealousy, neglect, hatred, selfish ambitions, stealing, lying, and greed to mention a few. It is also a sinful act if we know it is right to do something and fail to do it. For instance, all of us know it is right to incorporate physical exercise into our daily routine. Exercise is one of God's natural laws for the health and maintenance of our body. If you fail to do this, you are committing a sin.

What are the consequences of sin? The consequence of sin is eternal separation from God, punishment, pain, sickness, and disaster. God deplores disobedience and sends punishment our way to let us know we are wrong and to encourage us to change our ways. God blesses us when we follow His ways and punishes us when we ignore Him.

> Don't be misled. Remember that you can't ignore God and get away with it. You will always reap what you sow! Those who live only to satisfy their own sinful desires will harvest the consequences of decay and death. But those who live to please the Spirit will harvest everlasting life from the Spirit. So don't get tired of doing what is good. Don't get discouraged and give up, for we will reap a harvest of blessing at the appropriate time.
> **Galatians 6:7-9 (The New Living Translation)**

Most of the sickness that Americans suffer is self-induced. God created you, God owns you, and God expects you to be a good steward of all he has given you. Your health is no exception. It is your responsibility to nourish and maintain your mind and body for God's glory. The consequence of not taking care of yourself is decay, pain, sickness, and death.

> Don't you know that you yourselves are God's temple and that God's spirit lives within you? If anyone destroys God's temple, God will destroy him; for God's temple is sacred, and you are that temple.
> **1 Corinthians 3:16-17 (New International Version, NIV)**

You are the temple of God. Therefore honor God by taking care of your body, mind and spirit. The bible tells us that the body and mind will eventually die and decay. Only the spirit will transcend into the next world. This is true. The flesh will eventually die and decay. The fact that only the spirit has eternal life does not mean that you should neglect the flesh!

I find many Christians confused on this point. They work hard at developing the spirit, but neglect the flesh and dishonor God. I see so many Christians praying for health and healing, yet they will not take action to obey God's natural laws of good health. When you become a Christian, your eternal life begins immediately here on earth. As a Christian, you don't just sit back, do nothing and wait for physical death or Christ's return. You are to fulfil the will of God's spirit within you. The only way you can do the will of the spirit is through the actions of the body and mind.

This is why the synergy or working together of the body, mind and spirit is so important. The body and mind is lost without the spirit and the spirit is incapable of accomplishing God's will without the body and mind.

God has given us everything we need to maintain a long healthy life. He has given us the foods, water and oxygen we need to maintain a healthy vibrant life. It is your responsibility to follow His will and live a healthy lifestyle for the glory of God. Anything less is sinful and leads to the decay and destruction of your health.

> Seek his will in all you do, and he will direct your paths. Don't be impressed with your own wisdom. Instead, fear the LORD and turn your back on evil. Then you will gain renewed health and vitality.
> **Proverbs 3:6-8 (The New Living Translation)**

Lifestyle and Environmental Reasons for Sickness

Millions of people in America are negligent in following God's prescription for good health. Our body requires nutritious foods, physical exercise, adequate rest, and a clean nontoxic environment for good health. Unfortunately, the current situation in America is far from God's prescription for good health. Our unhealthy lifestyles and environmental destruction both contribute to our demise.

The current American lifestyle is hectic, fast paced and stressful. Our diet consists primarily of nutritionally depleted processed foods containing high amounts of fats and refined sugar.

Although very busy, we do not get the physical exercise required to maintain good health.

Ultimately, Americans pay the price for our abusive lifestyle – obesity, heart disease, cancer, stroke, diabetes, pain, suffering, etc.

A clean environment is the foundation of life on this planet. It is the basis for health in every organ, gland, and tissue in the body. Our body requires clean and nontoxic food to eat, water to drink, and air to breathe.

At the beginning of the twentieth century, planet earth was relatively pure and free of toxic chemicals. Beginning with the Industrial Revolution and during this Age of Technology, man has violated virtually every law of nature, every law of God. America has become a toxic waste dump. Our air, water and soil are polluted. As a result, man's health on all levels, physical, moral, mental, and social, is now weak and compromised. The sinful abuse of our environment manifests itself in escalating disease, pain and death.

It is our responsibility to be good stewards of our planet. All of us have contributed to this environmental holocaust either by direct contribution or by allowing others to pollute our environment. God is punishing all of us for these deeds through impaired health, unnecessary suffering, and early death.

The sinful nature of our American society has taken its toll on our health. Reckless industrialization, unchallenged power and greed, self-reliance, complacency, and rejecting God has diminished us to a sickly nation. America is a nation sick in body, mind and spirit.

A nation that turns their back to God will never really prosper. I'm sure God is weeping as He witnesses the demise of America. But, fortunately it is not too late. There is still hope. God loves you, He loves your family, and He loves America. You can make a difference. Repent, change your sinful ways, and follow God's ways. God wants to restore your health, your family, and your nation. It all starts with you. Will you accept His generous offer?

> Don't you realize that whatever you choose to obey becomes your master? You can choose sin, which

leads to death, or you can choose to obey God and receive his approval.
Romans 6:16 (The New Living Translation)

Section II - The Trinity of Humanity

Body, Mind and Spirit working together to produce a healthy individual for the glory of God

Body

Your body is a miraculous, complex machine that allows us to do God's will. God designed your body with specific requirements for maintaining optimum health. Your body needs adequate nutrients, physical exercise, and sleep/relaxation. Providing your body with these necessities leads to optimal health. Depriving your body of these necessities produces less than optimal health. In fact, inadequate nutrition, exercise, and sleep leads to illness and disease.

The following six chapters discuss these important requirements: Nutrition, Exercise and Sleep.

CHAPTER 5

Nutrition

What does the word nutrition mean to you? Nutrition is often confused with the word diet.

Diet refers to your eating habits. It's what you eat on a regular basis. The word diet or dieting in America is often misused to refer to a temporary program for losing body weight through starvation or bizarre eating habits. Your diet is your long-term eating program. It defines who you are. It defines your character and beliefs. Your diet reflects your personal relationship with God.

Nutrition is the act or process of providing nutrients. Providing adequate nutrients is a key to maintaining optimum health. Your diet may or may not be nutritious. Your diet may provide you with the nutrients you need for good health or it may not.

In your opinion, does the Standard American Diet (SAD) provide the necessary nutrients for optimum health? Based on our reduced longevity, health expenditures of over a trillion dollars and widespread obesity across America, I can emphatically say No! The Standard American Diet does not provide adequate amounts of nutrients to maintain good health.

Nutrient Requirements

Your body requires many different nutrients for optimum health. Keeping these essential nutrients in proper balance is the key to maintaining or regaining your health. The essential nutrients are:

- Protein
- Carbohydrates
- Fiber
- Fat
- Vitamins
- Minerals

- Phytochemicals
- Water
- Oxygen
- Sunlight

Protein

Your body needs protein for growth, repair, and to carry out thousands of metabolic reactions. All of the structural material within the body is built out of protein. Protein is the framework around which calcium and phosphorus are deposited to form bone. Hair, skin and nails are made of protein. Connective tissue, tendons, ligaments and cartilage are made of protein. Muscle fibers and internal organs are made of protein. Virtually every component of the body and every process that takes place within the body is dependent upon protein. Lack of quality protein is a serious problem that your body cannot cope with for long without permanent negative effects.

The building blocks of protein are amino acids. There are twenty different amino acids. Eleven of these amino acids are designated nonessential because your body synthesizes them. Nine of these amino acids are designated essential because your body cannot synthesize them and they must be present in your diet (see Table 5-1). Amino acids form protein by joining together in specific sequence forming long chains. Proteins are very large molecules and frequently are composed of several hundred amino acids bonded together.

Proteins are classified as complete and incomplete. Complete proteins are proteins that contain all the essential amino acids. Incomplete proteins are proteins that are lacking one or more of the essential amino acids. Complete proteins are found in animal products: meat, milk, cheese, and eggs. Protein found in some plant products such as rice and potato is also complete. Incomplete proteins are found in plant products: grains, kidney beans, peas, lima beans, seeds, and nuts. Not all plant products have incomplete proteins. Rice, potato, and soybeans contain complete proteins.

Essential and Nonessential Amino Acids

Essential Amino Acids	Nonessential Amino Acids
Histidine	Alanine
Isoleucine	Asparagine
Leucine	Aspartic Acid
Lysine	Arginine
Methionine	Cysteine
Phenylalanine	Glutamic Acid
Threonine	Glutamine
Tryptophan	Glycine
Valine	Proline
	Serine
	Tyrosine

Table 5-1

Not only should you consume protein that is complete, you should also consume protein that is digestible and usable for the growth and repair of your body. Not all sources of protein are equal in quality. There are a variety of methods for determining the quality of a protein. One of the best methods to measure the quality of protein is called the Biological Value of protein. Biological Value (BV) measures the efficiency with which essential amino acids are

incorporated into tissue protein. A BV of 100 is a perfectly balanced protein and is of the highest quality. Whole egg protein is a high quality protein and is used as the standard for rating quality protein. Refer to Table 5-2 for the BV of some commonly consumed proteins. As a general rule, proteins with a BV above 70 are considered good quality and can support life if they are the only proteins consumed. Those below 70 cannot be eaten as the only source of protein, since a low BV indicates that one or more essential amino acids are present in low quantities.

Biological Values of Some Common Proteins

Protein	BV
Whole Egg	96
Milk	85
Egg White	83
Rice (6% protein)	79
Fish	70
Beef	70
Soybeans	69
Whole Wheat	67
Potato (2% protein)	67
Wheat Flour	50
Navy Beans	38

Table 5-2

How much protein is required for daily consumption? Ten to fifteen percent of your daily calories should come from protein. A good general rule for determining daily protein requirements is one gram of protein for every kilogram (2.2 lbs.) of body weight. This is a general rule for an average adult. It does not take into account the quality of body weight considered; is it muscle? Fat? Is the person grossly underweight or overweight?

Pregnant or lactating women have a higher protein requirement. Children require more protein per pound of body weight than adults because of their rapid growth and development. Table 5-3 will give you a clearer guideline for protein requirements. These figures represent quality protein.

Daily Protein Requirements

Age Group	Daily Requirement
Under One Year	3.5 grams/2.2 lbs.
One to Three Years	40 grams
Four to Six years	50 grams
Seven to Nine Years	60 grams
Ten to Twelve Years	70 grams
Thirteen to Twenty Years	75 – 100 grams
Male Adult	70 – 100 grams
Female Adult	50 – 80 grams
Pregnant	85 – 100 grams
Lactating	100 – 200 grams

Table 5-3

Carbohydrates

The human body is designed to get our primary source of energy from carbohydrates. While our body can use protein and fat for energy, carbohydrates provide the easiest and most efficient way to generate our energy requirements. All carbohydrates are eventually broken down into a simple sugar called glucose. Glucose is our ultimate source of energy.

Carbohydrates are categorized as either simple or complex carbohydrates. Simple carbohydrates exist as single sugars called monosaccharides or double sugars called disaccharides. Examples of monosaccharides are glucose and fructose and examples of disaccharides are maltose, sucrose and lactose.

Complex carbohydrates are referred to as polysaccharides. A polysaccharide is chain of many monosaccharides. All polysaccharides are eventually broken down into the monosaccharide glucose. Examples of polysaccharides are glycogen and starch.

Sucrose, common table sugar, is a simple carbohydrate created through the refinement of sugar cane and is often misused leading to many health problems. When natural sugar cane is refined vitamins, minerals, enzymes and fiber are lost. This produces a highly concentrated sugar that passes quickly into the bloodstream giving the stomach and pancreas a shock. An acid condition forms that consumes the body's minerals quickly. Calcium is used to correct this acidic condition. The digestive system is weakened and food cannot be digested properly. This leads to a blood-sugar imbalance and to further craving for sugar.

Refined sugar delivers high energy, but unfortunately, it is addicting and contributes greatly to disease and unhappiness. Using large amounts of sugar leads to obesity, hypoglycemia, diabetes, high blood pressure, heart disease, anemia, immune deficiency, tooth decay, and bone loss. It contributes to herpes, yeast infections, cancer, pre-menstrual syndrome, menstrual problems, and male impotence. It weakens the mind, causing loss of memory and concentration, nervousness, shyness, violence, excessive talking, negative thoughts, paranoia, and emotional upsets such as self-pity, arguments, and irritability.

The consumption of refined sugar in the American diet has significantly increased over the last two centuries. In 1815 sugar consumption was about 15 pounds per person per year. Today sugar consumption is about 135 pounds per person per year. This nine-fold increase in sugar consumption is a major contributor to the deterioration of health in America today.

Refined sugar is pervasive in the processed foods we eat today. Major sources of added sugars are candies, desserts, cakes, pies, cookies, fruit drinks, soft drinks, ice cream, canned fruits, and breakfast cereals. You may not even know you are eating sugar because it comes under many different names (see Table 5-4).

Names For Added Sugars That Appear On Food Labels	
Brown Sugar	Malt Syrup
Cane Juice	Maltose
Corn Sweetener	Mannitol
Corn Syrup	Maple Syrup
Dextrose	Molasses
Fructose	Raw Cane
Fruit Juice Concentrate	Raw Sugar
Glucose	Sorbitol
High-Fructose Corn Syrup	Sucrose
Honey	Syrup
Invert Sugar	Table Sugar
Lactose	Turbinado Sugar
Levulose	Xylitol

Table 5-4

How much carbohydrate is required for daily consumption? Sixty to seventy percent of your daily calories should come from carbohydrate. Of this daily carbohydrate requirement eighty percent should come from complex carbohydrates and twenty percent from simple carbohydrates. Complex carbohydrates are the preferred form of carbohydrates because they take longer to digest and covert into glucose. Complex carbohydrates provide the body with a steady source of energy and avoids undesirable blood-sugar imbalances. Natural sources of simple carbohydrates are fruit and raw honey. Sources of complex carbohydrates include grains, vegetables, and beans.

As stated previously, all carbohydrates are converted to glucose, our primary source of energy. Glycogen is the body's form of stored glucose. Glycogen is stored within the liver and muscle tissues. When our supply of available glucose is depleted from exercise or emotional or physical stress, the body converts the stored glycogen back to glucose to maintain proper glucose levels in the blood.

The body's ability to store glucose in the form of glycogen is limited. All excess glucose that can no longer be stored as glycogen is converted to the fat triglyceride and stored as body fat. Therefore, it is important to keep in mind that a constant overdose of carbohydrate in the diet is a major cause of obesity.

Fiber

The body has several ways of cleansing itself and removing toxins or poisons. The fastest, most efficient way is through the lower digestive tract, specifically, the colon or large intestine. The majority of the body's waste material and potential toxins are passed through this canal. Maintenance of the colon is imperative for good health.

Physical discomforts and disorders, common to most people at one time or another, that signal potential problems in the waste elimination system include constipation, diarrhea, colitis, or diverticulitis. These annoying conditions all signal problems in the colon. The body also produces many potentially hazardous by-products of metabolism which, if allowed to remain in the colon for prolonged periods, may produce cancerous chemicals that act directly upon the walls of the colon.

Transit time is the time it takes for the body to pass the waste products through the colon and eliminate them. The normal healthy transit time for feces is about twenty-four hours. This regularity is achieved by including enough fiber in the daily diet.

Modern diets, consisting of over-processed foods contain little or no fiber material. All natural fiber is removed in the refining stages. Because of our low fiber diets, constipation is one of the most common complaints of people today. It is not uncommon to find many people with a feces transit time of forty-eight to ninety-six hours. This additional time of fecal retention sets up the perfect conditions for toxic materials to form. The body begins drowning in its own waste. It can be said that disease begins in the colon.

In order to maintain a healthy colon and proper transit time you must ingest not less than thirty-five grams of dietary fiber daily. The best natural sources of dietary fiber are whole grains, fruits, and vegetables. Although natural whole food sources of dietary fiber are preferred, good sources of supplemental fiber are bran fiber and psyllium husk powder. Refer to Table 5-5 for fiber content of selected foods.

Two types of dietary fiber are commonly found in foods – insoluble fiber and soluble fiber.

Insoluble fiber holds water and is found in most whole grains and seeds. While the body cannot digest this type of fiber due to lack of enzymes, insoluble fiber does contribute to reducing constipation. The health benefits of soluble fiber are softening of feces and acceleration of intestinal transit time.

Soluble fiber dissolves in water and results in the production of a gel. Food sources of this fiber are the pulp of fruits, vegetables, oat bran, and beans. The health benefits of insoluble fiber are lowering of blood cholesterol and decreasing the absorption rate of glucose aiding in blood glucose imbalances. Be sure to include plenty of fiber in your diet.

Fiber Content Of Selected Foods		
Food	**Serving Size**	**Total Fiber (gms)**
Fruits		
Apple, with skin	1 medium	4.2
Banana	1 medium	2.5
Blackberries	1 cup	8.8
Grapes	1 cup	0.6
Orange	1 medium	2.5
Peach	1 medium	2.3

Fiber Content Of Selected Foods		
Pear, Bartlett	1 medium	4.0
Prunes, dried	4	3.1
Red Raspberries	1 cup	9.2
Strawberries	1 cup	1.6
Vegetables		
Asparagus, cooked	½ cup	1.7
Broccoli, raw	½ cup	4.0
Brussel Sprouts, cooked	½ cup	3.6
Carrot, raw	1 medium	2.6
Cauliflower, raw	½ cup	1.0
Celery, raw	½ cup	4.0
Corn, cooked	½ cup	4.7
Green Beans, cooked	½ cup	2.0
Lettuce, Butterhead	1 cup	1.3
Lettuce, Iceberg	1 cup	1.0
Lettuce, Romaine	1 cup	0.7
Peas, cooked	½ cup	4.4
Pepper, Green, raw	½ cup	0.9
Potato, baked, with skin	1 medium	5.0
Sweet Potato, baked, peeled	1 medium	4.0
Sweet Potato, baked, with skin	1 medium	6.8
Summer Squash	½ cup	2.0
Tomato	1 medium	1.3
Zucchini, raw or cooked	½ cup	3.0
Beans and Peas (cooked)		
Black Beans	1 cup	19.4
Blackeyed Peas	½ cup	4.1
Garbonza Beans	½ cup	4.0
Kidney Beans	½ cup	8.2
Lentils	½ cup	4.5
Lima Beans	½ cup	5.8
Pinto Beans	½ cup	10.3
Breads/Rice/Pasta		
Bran Muffins	2 muffins	4.6
Pumpernickel Bread	1 slice	1.0
Rye Bread	1 slice	1.6
Sourdough Bread	1 slice	2.8

Fiber Content Of Selected Foods		
White Bread	1 slice	0.6
Whole Wheat Bread	1 slice	2.2
Brown Rice	½ cup	1.8
White Rice	½ cup	0.6
Wild Rice	½ cup	1.3
Spaghetti, Whole Wheat	1 cip	5.6
Spiral Pasta, cooked	1 cup	1.3
Spiral Pasta, Whole Wheat, cooked	1 cup	3.7
Nuts and Seeds		
Almonds	¼ cup	3.9
Cashews	¼ cup	1.1
Peanuts, dry roasted	¼ cup	2.5
Walnuts	¼ cup	1.4
Sesame Seeds	¼ cup	3.3
Sunflower Seeds	¼ cup	2.2
Breakfast Cereal		
All-Bran with Extra Fiber	½ cup	15.0
Bran Buds	1/3 cup	10.7
Bran Flakes	1 cup	5.0
Cherrios	1 cup	1.6
Corn Flakes	1 cup	0.7
Fiber One	½ cup	13.0
Oatmeal, cooked	1 cup	4.0
Shredded Wheat	1 cup	4.2
Total Raisin Bran	1 cup	6.0
Wheaties	1 cup	2.0

Table 5-5

Fat

Contrary to popular belief, fat is good for you! Eating the right kind of fat is not only good, but also vital for maintaining optimal health. Essential fats reduce the risk of cancer, heart disease, allergies, arthritis, depression, fatigue, immune system dysfunction and a whole lot more. It seems that the more fats are researched, the longer this list of benefits grows.

The nutrient group known as fats or lipids is composed of triglycerides, phospholipids, and sterols. Lipids have several beneficial roles in the body and are actually vital to good health. The important roles of lipids are:

Concentrated source of energy. Fat provides more than twice as much energy as carbohydrates and proteins. Fat provides 9 kilocalories(kcal)/gram(g) as opposed to 4 kcal/g for carbohydrates and protein.

Important component of cell membranes. Phospholipids and cholesterol are important structural components of cell membranes.

Aid absorption of fat-soluble vitamins. Fat-soluble vitamins A, D, E, and K cannot be absorbed into the blood and lymph unless fat is present.

Shock absorption for the body's organs. A layer of fat surrounds vital organs such as the kidneys, eyeballs, and heart for padding and protection.

Helps maintain body temperature. Fat located below the surface of the skin serves as insulation. This layer of fat helps the body maintain it's constant 98.6 degree temperature and protects from rapid heat loss during winter.

Component of various important chemical reactions. Bile located in the gallbladder emulsify or breakdown fats for fat digestion. All of the steroid hormones, such as estrogen and testosterone, and vitamin D are synthesized from cholesterol.

If fat is good for you, why is there so much commotion and confusion about eating fats in our diet? The commotion and confusion around dietary fats revolves around the issue that there are fats that heal and there are fats that kill. In our Western culture we eat too much of the kind of fat that kills and not enough of the fat that heals.

First of all, Americans eat too much fat. Fifteen to twenty percent of your daily calories should come from fats. Currently, the average American consumes a diet of at least forty percent fat. Inhabitants of countries that have a low incidence of fat-related disease, like Japan, Philippines, and Thailand, consume only fifteen to twenty percent of their daily calories from fat.

Secondly, Americans eat the wrong kind of fat. There are three categories of fat – saturated, monounsaturated, and polyunsaturated. Americans consume too much saturated fat from animal sources and not enough polyunsaturated fat from plants. Saturated and monounsaturated fatty acids are not essential nutrients. The body can manufacture them. On the other hand, polyunsaturated fatty acids are essential nutrients. They must be ingested because the body cannot manufacture them. They are required to maintain a healthy body. Saturated fats are the fats that kill and polyunsaturated fats are the fats that heal.

There are two essential polyunsaturated fatty acids required for good health – alpha-linolenic acid and linoleic acid. Alpha-linolenic acid is also referred to as an omega 3 essential fatty acid and linoleic acid as an omega 6 essential fatty acid. They cannot be synthesized by the body and must be consumed through your diet.

Saturated fatty acids form part of all cell membranes, but are mainly used as fuel for energy. Monounsaturated fatty acids are also used in our cell membranes and used as fuel for energy. In addition, when levels of the polyunsaturated essential fatty acids are deficient, monounsaturated fatty acids are converted to polyunsaturated fatty acids. These converted polyunsaturated fatty acids attempt to perform the functions of the essential omega 3 and omega 6 fatty acids, but fail to do so completely.

Essential fatty acids are not normally used as fuel for energy unless they are in excess. Primary functions of essential fatty acids include oxygen transfer, hemoglobin production, cell membrane components, recovery from fatigue, creation of hormone-like prostaglandins, growth, cell division, brain development in children, and enhancement of immune function.

Almost all foods that contain fat have a balance of the all three kinds of fat. A piece of meat contains mainly saturated and monounsaturated with little polyunsaturated fat. Olive oil has mainly monounsaturated fat. Flax seed oil has mainly polyunsaturated fat. See Figure 5-2 for a comparison of dietary fats.

Ideal fat consumption is fifteen to twenty percent of your daily calories. Based on twenty percent fat consumption, saturated, monounsaturated, and polyunsaturated fats should be equally proportioned – six percent saturated, seven percent monounsaturated, and seven percent polyunsaturated. Your polyunsaturated essential fats should consist of four percent omega 6 linoleic acid and three percent omega 3 alpha linolenic acid (see Figure 5-1).

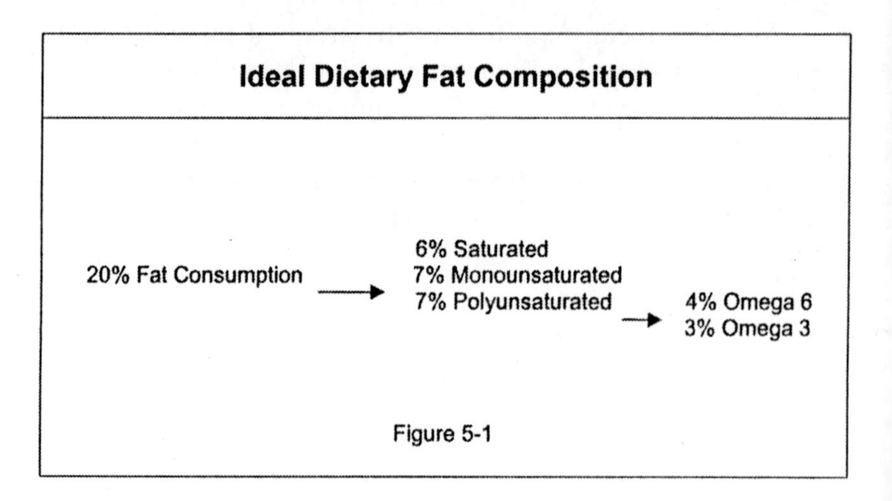

Figure 5-1

Of all the nutritional myths perpetuated today, perhaps there is none greater than the cholesterol scare. Even the subtle mention of the word brings panic and terror. Cholesterol levels are supposedly associated with cardiovascular disease, especially atherosclerosis or hardening of the arteries. Despite the evidence that there is no correlation between cholesterol and atherosclerosis, our medical community continues to perpetuate this myth.

The cholesterol scare is big business for doctors, laboratories, and drug companies. Drug therapy cholesterol-lowering measures in the United States is estimated at $60 billion annually, and is a very profitable scam considering that heart disease has not been reduced from these efforts.

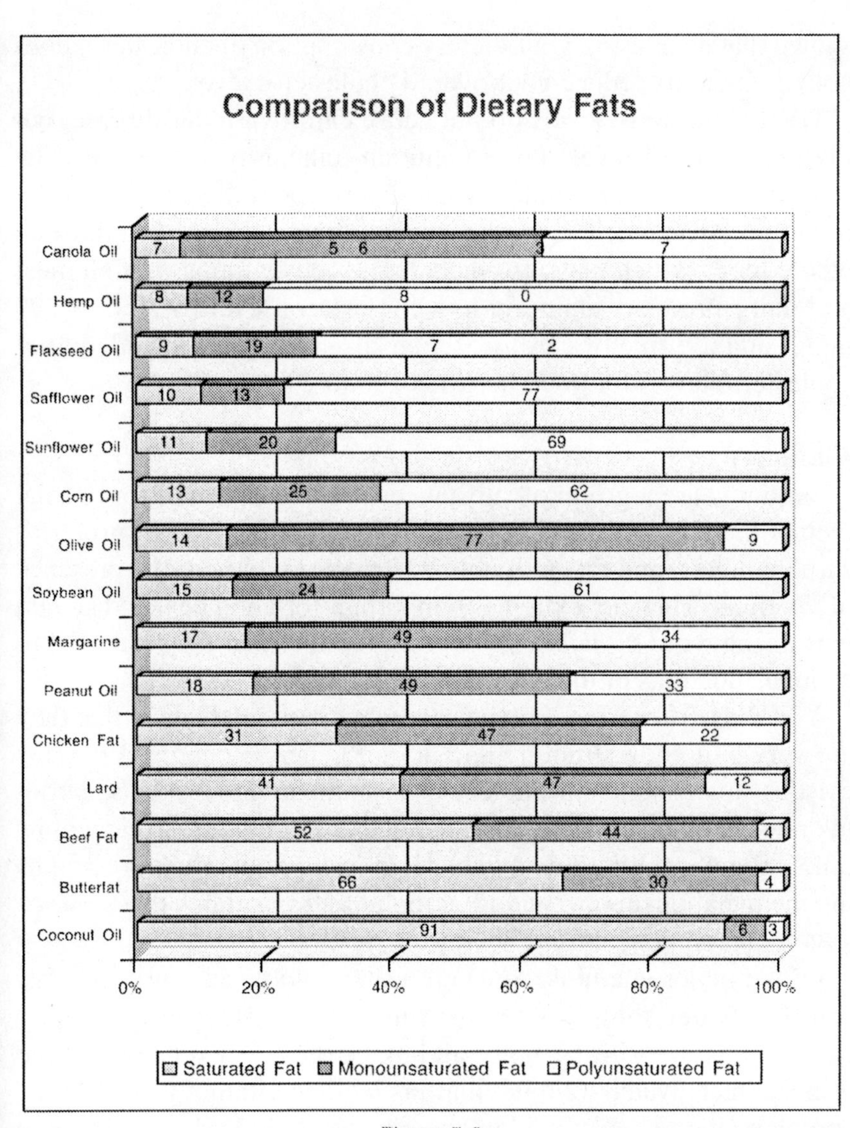

Figure 5-2

Cholesterol is so important, your body manufactures it daily. Cholesterol is manufactured primarily by the liver, but cholesterol is also manufactured in our cells, intestine, adrenal glands, and sex glands. Although your body can produce all the cholesterol it needs, it balances cholesterol production with cholesterol input from your diet. In other words, when you consume foods with cholesterol, your body produces less cholesterol. Research has shown that decreasing your dietary consumption of cholesterol does not significantly reduce your overall cholesterol level.

High cholesterol levels do not cause cardiovascular disease, but high cholesterol levels do indicate an unhealthy individual. The primary cause of high cholesterol levels is a poor diet and unhealthy lifestyle. African tribes whose normal diets consist of traditional whole foods which may also include the consumption of high meat and dairy products maintain low cholesterol levels of 150 to 180 mg/dl and are free of cardiovascular disease. Recommended total cholesterol levels for good health is 150 to 200 mg/dl.

Vitamins

Vitamins are a group of substances that are essential for normal metabolism, growth, and development. The functions of proteins, carbohydrates, and fats will not be performed without the presence of vitamins. They are extremely important for good health. The *vita* part of the word *vitamin* comes from the fact that they are vital to cellular functions of the body.

Vitamins differ from proteins, carbohydrates, and fats in that they are very simple in structure and do not generate energy. Vitamins exist as small single unit molecules as compared to proteins, carbohydrates, and fats that are large molecules composed of many units linked together. Vitamins do not yield energy but assist in regulating the metabolism of proteins, carbohydrates, and fats that serve as structural components and liberate energy.

Of the major vitamins, some are water-soluble and some are fat-soluble. Water-soluble vitamins must be ingested daily, as they cannot be stored in the body and any excess is excreted via the urinary tract. Water-soluble vitamins include vitamin C and the B-complex vitamins. Fat-soluble vitamins can be stored in the body in fatty tissue and the liver. Fat-soluble vitamins include vitamins A, D, E, and K.

Both types of vitamins are needed by the body for proper functioning. There are sixteen vitamins essential for good health (see Table 5-6).

Essential Vitamins For Good Health

Vitamin	Daily Dosage
Vitamin A	15,000 IU
Vitamin B_1 (Thiamine)	50 mg
Vitamin B_2 (Riboflavin)	50 mg
Vitamin B_3 (Niacin)	100 mg
Vitamin B_5 (Pantothenic Acid)	100 mg
Vitamin B_6 (Pyridoxine)	50 mg
Vitamin B_{12} (Cobalamin)	300 mcg
Vitamin C	2,000 mg
Vitamin D	400 IU
Vitamin E	400 IU
Vitamin K	140 mcg
Biotin	300 mcg
Choline	200 mg
Bioflavinoids	500 mg
Folic Acid	400 mcg
Inositol	100 mg

Table 5-6

Minerals

Every living cell in your body depends on minerals for structure and proper function. Minerals are needed for the formation of blood and bone, the proper composition of body fluids, the maintenance of healthy nerve function, and the regulation of muscle tone. Like vitamins, minerals function as coenzymes, enabling the body to perform its functions, including energy production, growth, and healing. Because all enzyme activities involve minerals, minerals are essential for the proper utilization of vitamins and other nutrients.

In order to maintain optimal health, the human body must maintain its proper chemical balance. This balance depends on the levels of different minerals in the body and especially the ratios of certain mineral levels to one another. The level of each mineral in the body has an effect on every other, so if one mineral is out of balance, all mineral levels are affected. If not corrected, this can start a chain reaction of imbalances that leads to illness and disease.

Minerals cannot be synthesized by the body. Therefore, minerals must be consumed through our foods and through supplements. Some 79 minerals have been detected in animal and human tissue. Thousands of studies provide support for considering 60 of these 79 nutrients to be essential (see Table 5-7). The area of mineral research in human nutrition is in its infancy. There is much to learn about the functions and requirements of these minerals in humans. Appendix B provides detailed information on the functions and daily requirements for the common minerals.

Essential Minerals For Optimal Health

Aluminum	Gold	Rhenium
Antimony	Hafnium	Rubidium
Arsenic	Gallium	Samarium
Barium	Germanium	Scandium
Beryllium	Holmium	Selenium
Bismuth	Iodine	Silica
Boron	Iron	Silver
Bromine	Lanthanum	Sodium
Calcium	Lead	Strontium
Cerium	Lithium	Sulphur
Cesium	Lutecium	Tantalum
Chloride	Magnesium	Terbium
Chromium	Manganese	Thulium
Cobalt	Molybdenum	Tin
Copper	Neodymium	Titanium
Dysprosium	Nickel	Vanadium
Erbium	Niobium	Ytterbium
Europium	Phosphorus	Ytrium
Fluorine	Potassium	Zinc
Gadolinium	Praseodymium	Zirconium

Table 5-7

Phytochemicals

Phytochemicals are chemical substances found in plants that are responsible for giving them color, flavor, and natural resistance to disease. Phytochemicals are essential compounds for preventing disease and promoting optimal health in humans. These beneficial nutrients are found in whole grains, fruits and vegetables. There are several thousand phytochemicals currently known to exist, but new ones are being discovered all the time. Tomatoes alone are estimated to contain 10,000 different phytochemicals.

Eating a diet rich in whole grains, fruits, and vegetables provides an abundance of health enriching phytochemicals. See Table 5-8 for examples of some phytochemicals and their food sources.

Phytochemicals		
Phytochemical	**Function**	**Food Source**
Allicin	Strengthens immune system and protects against cancer	Garlic and onions
Bioflavonoids	Protects against cancer	Citrus fruits, berries, grapes, cantaloupe, plums, tomatoes, and cherries
Capsaicin	Protects DNA from damage and promotes blood circulation	Hot peppers
Coumarin and Chlorogenic acid	Protects against cancer	Tomatoes, green pepper, pineapple, strawberries, and carrots
Ellagic acid	Protects against cancer	Strawberries, grapes, and raspberries
Genistein	Destroys tumors	Soybeans
Indoles	Strengthen immune system	Brussels sprouts, cauliflower, and cabbage
Lutein	Protects the eye against age-related macular degeneration	Spinach, kale, collard greens, romaine lettuce, leeks and peas
Lycopene	Protects against cancer and heart disease	Tomatoes

Phytochemicals		
Phytoestrogens	Protects against cancer and other hormonal-related diseases	Soybeans, wheat, licorice, alfalfa, fennel, citrus fruits, and celery
Polyphenol	Protects against cancer	Garlic, soybeans, green tea, strawberries, grapes, carrots, broccoli, brussels sprouts, and cauliflower
Saponins	Protects against cancer	Kidney beans, chickpeas, soybeans, and lentils
Sulforaphane	Protects against cancer	Broccoli, brussels sprouts, cauliflower, turnips, and kale

Table 5-8

Water

Water is second only to oxygen in importance to health. The human body is composed of about 70 percent water. Every cell in the body requires water to perform its essential functions, including digestion, circulation, and excretion. Water maintains system equilibrium, lubricates, flushes wastes and toxins, hydrates the skin, regulates body temperature, acts as a shock absorber for joints, and transports nutrients throughout the body for assimilation. Water cleanses the body inside and out. When the body gets enough water, it works at its peak. Fluid and sodium retention decrease, gland and hormone functions improve, the liver breaks down and releases more fat, and hunger is diminished.

Water is crucial to your health. In fact, the lack of water, referred to as dehydration, can trigger disease, induce excessive aging, and eventually cause death. The state of dehydration in the human body can be a cause of many different diseases, such as high blood pressure, high cholesterol, migraine headaches, asthma, colitis, adult-onset diabetes, heart pain, and arthritis.

Replacing water that is continually being lost through sweating and elimination is very important. To keep your body functioning at peak performance, it is necessary to drink at least eight 8-ounce glasses of quality water each day. While the body can survive without food for about forty days, the body can only survive without water for about four days.

Your body needs pure quality water, not just fluids. Fluids contain more than water, they also contain caffeine, alcohol, refined sugar, artificial sweeteners, preservatives, and additional chemicals that the body does not need nor want. Caffeine and alcohol are addictive drugs that have diuretic properties. In other words, caffeine and alcohol promote dehydration of the body through excessive water elimination. Alcohol, coffee, tea, soda, and caffeine-containing beverages do not count as water.

Water is vital to all plants, animals, and humans on earth. Yet, through man's mismanagement of this God given resource, water resources are polluted and contaminated and unhealthy to drink. Our water resources are polluted around the world, throughout the United States, and even in your community. The tap water you drink in your home or business from municipal water supplies is not safe to drink. Municipal water supplies are contaminated with cancer causing chemicals from pesticides, herbicides, fertilizers, and industrial waste. Most well water is also contaminated. In addition, many municipal water supplies are chlorinated and/or fluoridated which is also harmful to your health.

Chlorine was first used to disinfect water in the United States in the early 1900s. At the time, outbreaks of cholera and typhoid fever spread by the water system were common and severe. In fact, major U.S. cities were suffering 100 or more typhoid deaths per 100,000 persons. Within 10 years after chlorine was introduced into the water system, the death rate fell dramatically. Since then, chlorine has been a primary means of chemically treating water.

Although chlorine does disinfect our water supplies and protects us from some diseases, there is concern that our chlorinated water supply promotes other diseases. Since the 1970s there has been a growing concern that chlorine and chlorine by-products in our drinking water are responsible for various types of cancer, arteriosclerosis, some miscarriages, and some serious birth defects. Although there is mounting evidence that chlorinated drinking water is connected to these diseases, chlorine is still the primary means of chemically treating water.

Fluoridation of our drinking water may be one of the biggest political scams ever forced on the American public. Fluoride is a hazardous waste product produced by the aluminum and fertilizer industries, and during World War II, the military industry. Fluoride is classified more toxic than lead and just slightly less toxic than arsenic. Our governmental regulatory agencies have taken measures to remove lead from our air, water, and paints due their harmful effects on humans. Yet fluoride, which is more toxic than lead, is intentionally pumped into our water supply at concentrations up to 350 times more than the allowable levels of lead. Why is fluoride added to our drinking water?

Fluoride is added to our drinking water to prevent tooth decay. Unfortunately, the truth is fluoride does not reduce tooth decay. There is no evidence to support fluoride reducing tooth decay. Fluoride was the key chemical in atomic bomb production, according to declassified papers of the Manhattan Project, the U.S. military group that built the atomic bomb. Massive quantities of fluoride - millions of tons - were essential for the manufacture of bomb-grade uranium and plutonium for nuclear weapons throughout World War II. One of the most toxic chemicals known, the documents reveal that fluoride rapidly emerged as the leading chemical health hazard of the U.S atomic bomb program - both for workers and for nearby communities.

During World War II, Alcoa (Aluminum Company of America) accelerated production to meet the need for more war materials. At the end of World War II there were massive amounts of fluoride left to be disposed. Since fluoride is a hazardous waste material, disposal of it is very expensive. At this time, the U.S. Public Health Service began promoting water fluoridation.

Water fluoridation began in 1945 with the recommendation of the U.S. Public Health Service under the direction of the Treasury Secretary Andrew Mellon, a founder and major stockholder of Alcoa. Even though fluoride was a known highly toxic chemical that was detrimental to human health, the U.S. government felt it was more important to protect industry rather than the health of the American people.

Today fluoridation is banned in nearly all European countries, but not in the United States.

Fluoride is known to weaken the immune system, accelerate aging, and cause cancer, dental fluorosis (brown spots on the teeth), and skeletal fluorosis (impaired bone repair and maintenance leading to premature arthritis, osteoporosis, and bone fragility). Do not drink fluoridated water!

Since our local water supplies are all tainted with toxic contaminants, the only safe water for drinking is distilled water or reverse-osmosis water. Bottled distilled or reverse-osmosis water can be purchased at your local grocer or you can purchase a water distiller or reverse-osmosis unit for your home. Spring water is not an acceptable choice for drinking water. Water from springs can be as contaminated or even more contaminated than your local tap water.

Oxygen

Oxygen is the most vital nutrient of all. This element has a more fundamental role in the human body than vitamins, minerals, or any other nutrient. You can survive about forty days without food and about four days without water, but you can only survive about four minutes without oxygen.

Oxygen is responsible for many chemical reactions in the body including producing energy and heat through the combustion of carbohydrates and fats. Oxygen is also a purifier, helping eliminate wastes in the body. Oxygen destroys germs, viruses, parasites, fungi, and yeasts, and helps break down mucus, cysts, tumors, and arterial plaque.

Human health and existence is dependent upon ample sources of oxygen. It is interesting to note that geologists measured oxygen levels of tiny air bubbles trapped in ancient polar ice and found that back in the days of dinosaurs our atmosphere was fifty percent oxygen. By the beginning of the twentieth century atmospheric levels of oxygen had dropped to thirty eight percent. During the 1950s oxygen levels dropped to twenty one percent. Today our atmosphere contains nineteen percent oxygen. In urbanized areas oxygen levels are even lower, approximately ten to twelve percent.

Most plant, animals, and of course humans are aerobic organisms. Aerobic means requiring oxygen to survive and thrive. There are some bacteria, viruses, and fungi that are anaerobic organisms. They survive and thrive with little or no oxygen. Along with the dropping of atmospheric oxygen levels, diseases of anaerobic origin have appeared or drastically increased over the last twenty to thirty years. Cancer is one example. In the year 1900 cancer occurred in one out of every thousand people. Today cancer afflicts one out of three people. See Table 5-9 for examples of other anaerobic diseases.

Due to low atmospheric levels of oxygen, poor diet and slothful lifestyle our bodies are deficient in oxygen and are breeding grounds for anaerobic diseases. Cancer is an anaerobic disease. It thrives in low oxygen environments. Cancer cannot take root in a body that is highly oxygenated!

There are several ways you can increase and distribute oxygen throughout your body. First of all, physical activity, regular exercise is a major key to increasing oxygen levels in your body. Living outside metropolitan areas where the atmospheric oxygen levels are higher will provide better quality air to breathe. Oxygenate your house. Fill your house with plants. Plants give off oxygen as a by-product of photosynthesis. Finally, decrease the amount of meat you eat and increase the amount of fresh, raw vegetables. Meat requires more oxygen for complete metabolism and elimination of waste products than vegetables and reduces oxygen reserves.

Anaerobic Diseases of Humans

Disease	Year of Appearance
Herpes II (sexually transmitted herpes)	1978
Staphylococcus (Toxic Shock Syndrome)	1980
HIV (AIDs virus)	1982
EBV, CMV (chronic fatigue syndrome)	1982
Candida albicans ("Candida")	1982
Hanta Virus ("Four Corners Disease")	1993
E. coli (Toxic Shock Syndrome)	1993
Type A Streptococcus ("flesh-eating" Strep)	1994
Coccidioidomycosis ("Valley Fever")	1900 (35/yr) 1996 (2,426/yr)
Cancer (all types)	1900 (1/1000) 2000 (1/3)

Table 5-9

Sunlight

> In the beginning God created the heavens and the earth. Now the earth was formless and empty, darkness was over the surface of the deep, and the Spirit of God was hovering over the waters. And God said, "Let there be light," and there was light. God saw the light was good . . . .
>
> **Genesis 1:1-4 (New International Version, NIV)**

God created the sun, a gaseous mass consisting primarily of hydrogen and helium. By weight, the sun is 78 percent hydrogen, 20 percent helium, and 2 percent heavier elements such as oxygen, carbon, nitrogen, and iron. The sun, through thermonuclear processes, transforms hydrogen into helium and liberates energy in the form of electromagnetic radiation. This radiation emitted from the sun travels through space and penetrates the atmosphere of earth. Incoming energy from the sun is mostly in the form of ultraviolet rays (9 percent), visible light (41 percent), and infrared waves (50 percent).

Sunlight is a necessary requirement for life on earth. The sun provides the energy necessary for green plants to grow. Green plants provide food for animals and humans and for the animals that ultimately produce meat, milk, and eggs for us to eat. Without sunlight all life on earth would cease to exist and the earth would be dark, cold, and barren.

Not only does the sun provide light, heat, and energy to grow food, sunlight also plays an important role in human health. Sunlight, reaching us through our eyes and our skin is responsible for regulating and enhancing many body functions. The health promoting benefits from sunlight actually come from the ultraviolet rays. It is the ultraviolet rays that promote health, but also cause the reddening and burning of your skin when exposed to excess sunlight.

The skin that covers and protects us is the largest organ in our body. Sunlight penetrating our skin has many beneficial effects. Sunlight helps combat many skin ailments such as psoriasis, eczema, and acne. Sunlight irradiating our blood as it circulates through the capillaries of the skin by means of sunbathing can increase the oxygen-carrying capacity of the blood and ultimately increase the oxygen content of body tissues. Increasing the oxygen content of our blood and body tissues is beneficial to our health. Sunlight also has a relaxing effect on the capillaries resulting in an overall lowering of blood pressure.

Sunlight absorbed by your skin is responsible for the synthesis of vitamin D from cholesterol. When released through the body and activated, vitamin D improves our efficiency in the metabolism of minerals such as calcium and magnesium, and also of protein. A Russian study found that vitamin D produces a thirty per cent improvement in our conservation of protein. Vitamin D is an important factor in the growth and development of bones and teeth. The transformation of vitamin D from cholesterol actually helps lower cholesterol levels in the body.

Sunlight strengthens our immune system. There are cells in our skin called keratinocytes that when stimulated by sunlight produce a chemical called interleukin-1. Interleukin-1 stimulates T-cell production which helps protect our body from internal foreign invaders like bacteria, viruses, and fungi. Sunlight also kills external bacteria, viruses, and fungi on our skin.

Whether we are office workers or athletes in training, the effects of ultraviolet light on fitness are considerable. One example is the improvement in the power, endurance and recovery time of muscles – and this includes the heart muscle. Fitness training undertaken in sunlight is far more effective than without it.

When the skin is exposed to sunlight, the blood passing through it receives ultraviolet radiation. The capacity of the blood to carry oxygen goes up. At the same time the amount of oxygen being supplied to the tissues increases. The effect of ultraviolet exposure lasts for hours or even days. When fueled with ultraviolet light energy, the blood becomes a living battery, supplying potential energy to the muscles and nerves.

The muscles underlying an area exposed directly to sunlight also show some beneficial effects. There is an increase in the amount of blood flowing through the muscles, as the blood vessels relax. At the same time the work capacity and endurance of the muscle goes up. The ancient Greeks were well aware of the athletic enhancing effects of sunlight. Greek athletes would train naked in the sunlight to expose all their muscles to ultraviolet light.

Absorbing sunlight through the retina of our eyes stimulates the pineal gland that is located in the middle of our brain. The pineal gland is our master gland responsible for the production of a hormone called melatonin and regulating the entire endocrine system. Melatonin and other hormones produced by the endocrine glands have powerful effects on the way our minds and bodies function. The pineal regulates our endocrine system by controlling the output of the pituitary gland. This small gland at the base of the brain produces hormones that control the functioning of all the other endocrine glands, and thereby of every cell in the body.

A good example of sunlight affecting our well being is its effect on our thyroid gland. Exposure to sunlight stimulates the output of our thyroid gland. Since the thyroid hormones regulate the metabolic rate, this can have a dramatic effect on the way we feel. Patients with even mild hypothyroidism (low thyroid hormone output) often feel chronically fatigued, rundown, unable to concentrate, generally unwell, and in need of excessive sleep. They also tend to put on weight, which can depress them still further. Sunlight, through the pineal-pituitary axis, can increase the output of the thyroid gland and remedy these problems.

God designed our body to feed on sunlight, and we suffer if starved of it. You should aim to nourish yourself with sunlight regularly, every week of the year. Regular exposure to sunlight, or to indoor lighting that includes the full spectrum of visible and ultraviolet light, can help us to get fitter and to look and feel better. All the crucial biological processes dependent on sunlight hitting the skin are activated and sent to the rest of the body. Fitness in general and cardiovascular fitness in particular improves. We are able to build healthier muscles with greater endurance, to use up more calories more efficiently and to burn off fat deposits. All of these changes enable us to feel and look better.

> Light shines on the godly, and joy on those who do right.
> **Psalms 97:11 (The New Living Translation)**

There are many different nutrients required for good health. Unfortunately, most people are not familiar with these nutritional requirements. Health and nutrition is not taught at this detail in our public schools. Your parents never taught you about nutrition because they don't know about proper nutrition either. As long as sickness and disease is big business in America, proper health and nutrition will never be part of our mainstream education. Conglomerate food manufacturers, the health care industry, the pharmaceutical industry, and the American government would all prefer that you remain ignorant about taking care of your own health.

Knowing God's truth about health and nutrition is the start of a happy and healthy life. Now put it into action. You don't need to remain sick and unhealthy anymore. You can make a change in your life and take control of your health. God wants you to be healthy, but you have to do it His way!

> A wise person is hungry for truth, while the fool feeds on trash.
> **Proverbs 15:14 (The New Living Translation)**

CHAPTER 6

Anti-Nutrients

The Standard American Diet consists primarily of hamburgers, hot dogs, fried chicken, french fries, chips, soda, cookies, pastries, ice cream and candy. These foods are highly processed, high in calories, fat and refined sugar and low in nutrients. These foods are not only void of nutrients, they contain undesirable compounds or anti-nutrients which work against optimum health. Examples of anti-nutrients are hydrogenated fats and oils, refined sugar, food additives, food preservatives and food colorings. In many cases these anti-nutrients are toxic to our body promoting illness or disease.

There are many food products that you commonly consume that contain anti-nutrients. Avoiding these food products will improve your health and vitality. A brief discussion of the primary anti-nutrients is warranted to help you beware of these health-robbing compounds lurking in our food supply.

Hydrogenated or Partially Hydrogenated Fats and Oils

Processed foods often contain hydrogenated or partially hydrogenated oils. These are liquid vegetable oils that are processed to make them solid or semi-solid. This process produces a new artificially created byproduct called trans fatty acids. Trans fatty acids have detrimental effects on our cardiovascular system, immune system, reproductive system, energy metabolism, fat and essential fatty acid metabolism, liver function, and cell membranes. Avoid margarines, shortenings, partially hydrogenated vegetable oils and food products containing these fats and oils.

Refined Sugar

Refined sugar is a worthless food substance that has been stripped of any nutritional value. Refined sugar comes in different forms (see Table 5-4), but all are void of vitamins, minerals, and enzymes necessary for proper metabolism. High sugar consumption contributes to a wide range of diseases, including cardiovascular disease, diabetes, arthritis, tooth decay, hypoglycemia, and osteoporosis. Consumption of refined sugar also contributes to mineral depletion, moodiness, and weight gain. Excess sugar in the body is stored as fat. Since Americans are addicted to sugar, nearly every processed food has sugar added to it. Minimize your sugar consumption. Cookies, cakes, candy, pies, ice cream, soft drinks, and breakfast cereals are usually very high in sugar content.

As an alternative to sugar, try using *Stevia rebaudiana* an herb that is thirty times sweeter than sugar. Stevia comes in powder or liquid extract. Just a few drops of extract will sweeten a cup of liquid. Stevia can also be used in cooking and baking.

Coffee

Coffee is a widely used beverage consumed for its stimulant effects. Caffeine is the stimulant ingredient. The ideal use of coffee is as an external remedy. A compound of wet grounds will speed the healing of bruises and insect stings. The safest internal use of coffee is as an enema in cases of constipation, asthma and cancer. There is nothing in coffee that your body needs!

Problems associated with coffee consumption:

1. Caffeine is an addictive stimulant which can produce any of several symptoms such as anxiety and nervousness, insomnia or light sleep patterns, various types of heart disease, stomach and intestinal problems, and moodiness. When consumed regularly, as little as two cups of coffee per day can initiate these symptoms.

2. Dangerous chemicals are used in the production of coffee: poisonous herbicide and pesticide sprays in its cultivation, petroleum-based solvents in its decaffeination, and other chemicals in making it instant; in addition, the oils in coffee easily go rancid once it is ground.

3. Coffee drinkers may be at risk of developing specific

diseases. Women who consume coffee on top of a high fat diet have a higher risk of breast and bladder cancer. Coffee consumption during pregnancy increases the rate of miscarriages and birth defects. Coffee intake is directly related to pancreatic cancer and heart attack. Moderate coffee drinking of two daily cups or more raises cholesterol. The more coffee consumed, the greater the likelihood of these conditions!

4. The acid in coffee eats away the villi, or nutrient absorbing components of the small intestines, reducing their effectiveness in supporting nutrient assimilation. Most heavy coffee drinkers are deficient in calcium and other minerals.

Avoid drinking coffee. Drink water and herbal teas.

Tobacco

Tobacco contains a mood-altering drug called nicotine. Nicotine acts as a stimulant on the central nervous system. Nicotine has long been known to be a deadly toxin. A single pinhead-sized drop of liquid nicotine, introduced directly into the bloodstream, would be fatal. At doses normally ingested by smokers, nicotine makes the heart pump faster and work harder, increasing the likelihood of heart disease. Besides nicotine, cigarettes contain over 4,000 chemical substances, and at least 43 of these substances are known to cause cancer in humans. Tobacco smoking causes an estimated one third of all cancer deaths, one fourth of fatal heart attacks, and 85 percent of deaths from lung cancer. Many other health problems are linked to smoking. These health problems include heart pain, hardening of the arteries, cataracts, bronchitis, colorectal cancer, diarrhea, emphysema, heartburn, high blood pressure, impotence, ulcers, respiratory ailments, circulatory ailments, and cancer of the mouth and throat.

Whether smoking, chewing, or sniffing, consumption of tobacco poses a health hazard.

The health hazards of tobacco are not limited to tobacco consumers. Passive or secondhand smoke from cigarette smoking is just as dangerous if not more dangerous than the smoke that smokers breathe. Fortunately, more and more work and public places are becoming smoke free. Do not use any tobacco products and avoid places where people are smoking.

Alcohol

Alcohol is a potent nonprescription drug sold to anyone over the national legal drinking age. No drug in the history of mankind has caused more illness, pain, despair, tragedy, broken families, and death than alcohol. Alcohol use is involved in:

- One-half of all murders, accidental deaths, and suicides
- One-third of all drownings and boating and aviation deaths
- One-half of all crimes
- Almost half of all fatal automobile accidents

Approximately sixty percent of American population consumes alcoholic beverages. One in ten people can expect to have a problem with alcohol consumption.

Alcohol is considered a food because it provides a concentrated number of calories, but it is not nourishing. Alcohol provides nothing that your body needs for good health. In fact, when ingested, alcohol is a poison to the body. Your liver breaks down toxic alcohol into carbon dioxide and water. Some of the health effects of long-term alcohol consumption include damage to the brain, cirrhosis of the liver, heart disease, cancer, and reduction in longevity usually by ten to fifteen years.

Although occasional use of alcohol by people in good health seems to pose no health risks, I recommend not consuming any alcohol at all. Possible addiction to alcohol and the chance of having alcohol related problems pose an unpredictable risk not worth taking. People who do not consume alcohol will never become alcoholics or have alcohol related problems.

Some proponents of alcohol consumption use the Bible to substantiate their alcohol use. The drinking of wine in Biblical times was indeed common. But do not be fooled, the wine of Biblical times was very different than the wine of today. The wine of Biblical times was not much more than fruit juice, only one to two percent alcohol. The wine of today is much more potent with ten to twelve percent being alcohol. The Bible also warns us about alcoholism.

Don't be drunk with wine, because that will ruin your life. Instead, let the Holy Spirit fill and control you.
Ephesians 5:18 (The New Living Translation)

Salt

Sodium, as found in salt, is a mineral of great importance to your health. Sodium is essential for water regulation, nerve transmission, muscle contraction, and maintenance of acid-base balance. Unfortunately, Americans consume far too much of it. Although the human body needs only 500 mg of sodium per day to stay healthy, our consumption averages over 8,000 mg per day.

Salt is second only to sugar as the most popular food additive. Fresh fruits and vegetables are low in sodium, whereas processed foods are generally high in sodium. For example, three and a half ounces of fresh, raw green peas have 2 mg of sodium, while three and a half ounces of canned green peas have 236 mg of sodium.

Excessive sodium intake can cause fluid to be retained in the body tissues, which can lead to high blood pressure and can aggravate many medical disorders, including congestive heart failure, certain forms of kidney disease, and premenstrual syndrome (PMS). Excessive sodium intake also causes the body to lose calcium in the urine, thus contributing to osteoporosis.

The best ways to limit your salt consumption is to avoid using salt when cooking and dining, and avoid processed foods that contain high amounts of sodium.

Artificial Sweeteners

A good rule to follow is to avoid all artificial sweeteners. These are man-made products of no nutritional value and detrimental to your health. The most popular and probably the most dangerous is aspartame.

Aspartame is the technical name for the brand names, NutraSweet, Equal, Spoonful, and Equal-Measure. Aspartame is the most dangerous substance on the market that is added to foods. Aspartame is a chemical poison made up of three chemicals: Aspartic acid, phenylalanine, and methanol (wood alcohol).

Aspartame is commonly marketed as a dieting additive because it is 200 times sweeter than sugar and contains no calories. Unfortunately, food manufacturers are playing a cruel joke on the American public. Aspartame is added to foods not to help you lose weight, but to make you overeat! Aspartame actually stimulates your appetite. In addition, there are many adverse reactions associated with aspartame.

Aspartame accounts for over 75 percent of the adverse reactions to food additives reported to the US Food and Drug Administration (FDA). Many of these reactions are very serious including seizures and death as disclosed in a February 1994 Department of Health and Human Services report. A few of the 90 different documented symptoms listed in the report as being caused by aspartame include:

> Headaches/migraines, dizziness, seizures, nausea, numbness, muscle spasms, weight gain, rashes, depression, fatigue, irritability, tachycardia, insomnia, vision problems, hearing loss, heart palpitations, breathing difficulties, anxiety attacks, slurred speech, loss of taste, tinnitus, vertigo, memory loss, and joint pain.

According to researchers and physicians studying the adverse effects of aspartame, the following chronic illnesses can be triggered or worsened by ingesting of aspartame:

> Brain tumors, multiple sclerosis, epilepsy, chronic fatigue syndrome, parkinson's disease, alzheimer's, mental retardation, lymphoma, birth defects, fibromyalgia, and diabetes.

Aspartame is added to over 9,000 food products even though it is not fit for human consumption. Aspartame can be found in:

- instant breakfasts
- breath mints
- cereals
- sugar-free chewing gum
- cocoa mixes
- coffee beverages
- frozen desserts
- gelatin desserts
- juice beverages
- laxatives
- multivitamins
- milk drinks

- pharmaceuticals and supplements
- shake mixes
- soft drinks
- tabletop sweeteners
- tea beverages
- instant teas and coffees
- topping mixes
- wine coolers
- yogurt

Avoid all food products with aspartame. Beware of food labels that say "Sugar Free". They usually contain aspartame. Food products containing aspartame are technically sugar free but still harmful to your health. Aspartame is in no way beneficial, this man-made chemical is toxic to your health and is only produced to create a wealth of profit for food manufacturers. Aspartame is a product of greed. Do not consume it, lest it consume you!

Our Depleted Food Supply

Have you ever heard the statement "You can get all the nutrients you need from the foods you eat?" Unfortunately, this is a fictitious statement bantered by many ignorant and misguided people. If you ever hear any health or medical professional make this statement, forgive them, for they know not what they say, and stay clear of them! Our current food supply does not supply adequate nourishment to maintain optimal health. Indeed, it is God's plan that His food shall provide all the nutrients we need to maintain our health. This is no longer the case. Our foods are depleted of essential vitamins and minerals and plentiful in toxic man-made chemicals, food additives, and preservatives.

Our agricultural practices and modern food processing techniques are primarily responsible for the poor quality of our foods and ultimately the 1.3 trillion-dollar health care costs of this nation. Nutrient depleted and toxic foods causing malnutrition and toxic overload in Americans is a major cause of our poor health.

In Exodus 23:10-11, God instructs us to plant and harvest our crops for six years, but let the land rest and lie fallow (bare) during the seventh year. As you might imagine, this is very wise instruction. Crops use and remove minerals from the soil. After six years of continuous use, soils become depleted of essential minerals and can no longer support bountiful harvests. God has revealed to man that in order to grow healthy, vibrant, and nourishing crops, the soil must contain abundant minerals. The land must remain dormant during the seventh year to allow the land to revitalize itself. I shared with you earlier that we need 60 minerals for good health. Plants are our main source for acquiring these minerals. Plants absorb the minerals from the soil and we ingest the minerals by consuming the plants.

Modern agricultural practices have departed from God's plan to allow the land to rest and revitalize every seven years. Man has turned from God and embraced man-made chemical fertilizers, herbicides, pesticides, and fungicides. Farmers no longer let the land lay fallow. Crops are planted and harvested year after year. As a result of our self-reliance, we now have mineral depleted soils yielding mineral depleted and toxic crops.

Modern day food processing and manufacturing has also degraded the quality of our foods. Processed foods are foods that have been changed. These are foods that are no longer in the form in which they are found in nature. Some processed foods have never been in the state of nature. Instead, they are fabricated in laboratories from man-made chemicals.

Processed foods are terrible things for your body for two reasons – they are stripped of their nutrient value in the refining process, and they are poisoned by adding sugar, fat, salt and other harmful additives.

Whole wheat is a very nutritious food. Yet, by refining whole wheat to make white flour, most of the nutrients are lost. The milling process destroys 40% of the chromium, as well as 86% of the manganese, 89% of the cobalt, 68% of the copper, 78% of the zinc, and 48% of the molybdenum. By the time whole wheat is completely refined, it has lost most of its phosphorus, iron, and thiamine, and much of its niacin and riboflavin. Refined whole wheat flour has also lost most of its fiber, vitamin E, important oils and amino acids.

Our food supply is severely depleted of nutrients. It is impossible to obtain all the nutrients you need to maintain a healthy mind and body from the food you eat. Therefore, dietary supplementation is imperative for optimal health.

Man is constantly trying to play God by attempting to reproduce

His foods less costly and more quickly. Man's attempts at this have been disastrous. Instead of nourishing our body with healthy, nutritious foods that God created, Americans indulge in toxic and nutrient depleted foods that man created. Will man ever stop competing against God, and start working with God? Our sinful nature makes it difficult, but not impossible. You can make a decision right now to repent, turn from your rebellious ways and start following God's ways. In your own words tell God right now that you want to change your ways and you need His help. God is always listening!

> There is a way that seems right to a man, but in the end it leads to death.
> **Proverbs 14:12 (New International Version, NIV)**

CHAPTER 7

Acid-Alkaline Balance

Keeping your body chemistry in balance is important for good health. One way to monitor the overall biochemical impact of your daily diet and lifestyle is to evaluate your acid-alkaline balance. Acid-alkaline balance is expressed in terms of pH. Potential hydrogen, or pH, refers to the acid or alkaline nature of your body fluids such as blood, saliva, and urine.

The pH of water is 7.0 and is considered neutral. In other words, at a pH of 7.0, the acid and alkaline components are in equal balance. A pH of less than 7.0 is considered acid and a pH greater than 7.0 is considered alkaline.

The acid-alkaline balance of your body fluids is not only important for good health, it is critical for life itself. The pH of your blood is between 7.35 and 7.45. This means that your blood is slightly alkaline. This alkalinity must remain constant for even minor variations are dangerous. If the hydrogen ion concentration of your blood pH rises to 6.95, just barely over the neutral line on the acid side, coma and death result. And, if the hydrogen ion concentration of your blood pH falls to 7.7, convulsions and death occur. With acid blood, the heart relaxes and ceases to beat, and with too alkaline blood, the heart contracts and ceases to beat.

Nearly all degenerative diseases including cancer, heart disease, arthritis, osteoporosis, kidney and gall stones, and tooth decay are associated with excess acidity in the body.

Table 7-1 lists many of the common symptoms and diseases associated with acidosis or excess acidity in the body.

Your acid-alkaline balance is maintained by a combination of diet and lifestyle. From a nutritional standpoint, foods are classified as either acid-forming or alkaline forming according to the effect they have on the body. In general, animal products and grains are acid forming and fruits and vegetables are alkaline forming (see

Table 7-2 for a listing of acid and alkaline forming foods). Our lifestyle also plays a role in acid-alkaline balance. Excessive exercise, stress, worry, anxiety, and anger all generate acids in the body which contribute to the overall acid-alkaline balance.

Common Symptoms of Acidosis		
Acne	Fatigue	Joint Pain
Hyperactivity	Food Allergies	Lack of Sex Drive
Diarrhea	Constipation	Arthritis
Excess Head Mucous	Depression	Loss of Memory
Migraine Headaches	Insomnia	Asthma/Bronchitis
Impotence	Excessive Hair Loss	Schizophrenia
Cancer	Multiple Sclerosis	Tuberculosis
Systematic Lupus Erythematosis	Hard Getting Up In The Morning	Bacterial/Viral/ Fungal Infections
Cystitis	Hay Fever	Psoriasis

Table 7-1

The first step in establishing a healthy alkaline diet is to evaluate your current pH. A good measure of average body pH is easily obtained by measuring the pH of your first morning urine. To do this, follow these steps:

Obtain a packet of pH hydrion test paper. This test tape measures acid-alkaline states and should provide a pH reading range from at least 5.5 to 8.0. pH testing tape should be available at your local pharmacy or natural food store.

First thing in the morning, before your first urination, cut off a strip of test paper approximately two inches in length. Now wet the test tape with urine.

The test strip will take on a color based on the pH of your urine. The color will range from yellow to dark blue and indicates your acid-alkaline state. Match the color of your test strip to the color chart on the test tape packet.

Ideally, the first morning urine pH should read 6.5 to 7 (an occasional 7.5 to 8 is okay). When the first morning urine is neutral of just slightly acidic, this indicates that the overall cellular pH is appropriately alkaline.

If your reading falls below 6.5, you should make changes to your diet by consuming more alkaline forming foods and less acid forming foods. Since the Standard American Diet is generally acid forming, most people will have low pH readings of less than 6.5. On the other hand, if your pH reading is consistently higher than 7, you should make changes to your diet by consuming more acid forming foods and less alkaline forming foods.

As a general rule to replenish and sustain your alkaline reserves, follow the 80/20 rule. This means that 80 percent of your foods are alkaline forming and 20 percent of your foods are acid forming. Research and clinical experience have reconfirmed this ideal ratio of 80/20. In fact practitioners as far back as Hippocrates (460 - 377 BC) have been using this ratio to heal virtually every condition known. To accomplish this ratio, 8 out of 10 foods should be alkaline forming. The remaining 2 out of 10 foods should be acid forming.

Be patient and persistent. Do not get discouraged. It can take time to build up your alkaline reserves to the point where you can maintain an ideal urine pH reading of 6.5 to 7. Eat more fruit and vegetables and less meat and processed foods. This is God's way!

> Those who obey Him will not be punished. Those who are wise will find a time and a way to do what is right.
> **Ecclesiastes 12:13 (The New Living Translation)**

Acid-Alkaline Food Chart

	High Alkaline Forming	Medium Alkaline Forming	Low Alkaline Forming	Neutral	Low Acid Forming	Medium Acid Forming	High Acid Forming
FRUITS	Cantaloupe Dates (dried) Figs (dried) Lemons Limes Mangos Melons Papaya Watermelon	Apricots Avocados Bananas Berries Dates (fresh) Figs (fresh) Grapes Grapefruit Kiwis Nectarines Passion Fruit Pears Pineapple Raisins Tangerines	Apples Cherries Olives Oranges Peaches Raspberries Strawberries		Blueberries Cranberries Plums Prunes		
VEGETABLES	Kelp Parsley Seaweed Watercress	Asparagus Carrots Celery Chard, Swiss Dandelion Greens Endive Escarole Leafy Lettuce Rutabaga Spinach	Bamboo Shoots Beets Broccoli Brussell Sprouts Cabbage Cauliflower Collard Greens Corn Cucumbers Eggplant Ginger Kale Mustard Greens Okra Onions Parsnips Pickles Potatoes Pumpkin Radishes Squash Turnips Water Chestnuts Herbs Spices	Artichokes Horseradish Mushrooms Rhubarb Sauerkraut Tomatoes			
BEANS			Green (fresh) Lima (fresh) Peas (fresh) Snap (fresh) String (fresh)	Soybeans	Aduki Black Garbanzo Kidney Lentils Mung Navy Pinto Red White		

Acid-Alkaline Food Chart

	High Alkaline Forming	Medium Alkaline Forming	Low Alkaline Forming	Neutral	Low Acid Forming	Medium Acid Forming	High Acid Forming
NUTS			Almonds Coconut (fresh)	Chestnuts	Brazil Cashews Coconut (dried) Filberts Macadamia Pecans Pistachios Walnuts	Peanuts	
OILS				Almond Avocado Coconut Canola Corn Olive Safflower Sesame Soy Sunflower			
GRAINS				Amaranth Millet Quinoa	Barley Corn Meal Rye Spelt	Brown Rice Buckwheat Oats Whole Wheat	Bleached Wheat White Rice
DAIRY				Whole Egg (soft yolk)	Butter Cheese Cow's Milk Cream Egg Whites Goat's Milk Yogurt	Whole Egg (Hard Yolk)	
MEATS						Fish	Beef Chicken Deer Goat Lamb Pheasant Turkey
SUGARS			Brown Rice Syrup Dried Sugar Cane Juice Honey (raw) Maguey		Barley Malt Syrup Fructose Honey (processed) Maple Syrup Turbinado	Molasses	Artificial Sweeteners Beet Cane

Acid-Alkaline Food Chart

	High Alkaline Forming	Medium Alkaline Forming	Low Alkaline Forming	Neutral	Low Acid Forming	Medium Acid Forming	High Acid Forming
MISC	Cayenne Pepper Baking Soda	Garlic	Apple Cider Vinegar Sea Salt		Popcorn	Wine Ketchup Mayonnaise Mustard Soy Sauce	Alcohol Beer Coffee Soft Drinks Caffeine Drinks Table Salt White Vinegar Drugs Tobacco Cakes Pies Pastries Candy Ice Cream

Table 7-2

CHAPTER 8

Dietary Laws

God has given us dietary laws to instruct us on how to provide the essential nutrients for our health and well being. In Genesis 1:29, God said "I give you every seed-bearing plant on the face of the whole earth and every tree that has fruit with seed in it. They will be yours for food." (NIV) The early patriarchs of the Bible were vegetarians. They ate fruits, vegetables, and grains as their food. After the great flood of Noah's time, God added animal flesh to our diet. Genesis 9:3 says, "Everything that lives and moves will be food for you. Just as I gave you the green plants. I now give you everything" (NIV).

About a thousand years later, when the Torah was given to Moses, God went into great detail and listed which animals were fit for human consumption (clean) and which were not fit for human consumption (unclean). The entire 11th chapter of Leviticus is devoted to this subject. A shorter version of the list is repeated in Deuteronomy 14. Genesis does not tell us which animals were fit or unfit for human consumption, but Genesis 7:2 and 8:20 tells us that Noah knew the difference.

In Deuteronomy 14:6, God tells us that we may eat any animal that has a split hoof divided in two and that chews the cud. It is interesting to note that the land dwelling animals acceptable as food are plant-grazing vegetarians with multiple stomachs or digestive chambers. Animals with multiple stomachs tend to detoxify and digest their food more completely than animals with a single stomach. The flesh of these animals tends to be less toxic for human consumption. Animals such as cattle, buffalo, sheep, goat, and deer are acceptable as food.

On the other hand, animal flesh that we are to avoid does not have a split hoof divided in two and/or does not chew their cud. A large portion of this group includes meat eating or refuse eating animals. These animals were not created to provide food but to be scavengers of the earth. Their digestive tract is less complex resulting in a more toxic flesh. Their role is to keep our environment clean not to serve as food. Animals such as swine, cats, dogs, lions, tigers, and leopards are not acceptable as food. Plant eating animals that belong to this group of animals not fit for human consumption include the horse, rabbit, llama, ape, monkey, mouse, and donkey.

In Deuteronomy 14:9, God tells us that of all the creatures living in the water, we may eat any that has fins and scales. This eliminates catfish, shark, shrimp, lobster, crayfish, and shellfish. They are all toxic scavengers designed to keep our environment clean.

God tells us in Deuteronomy 14: 13-20 which fowl are acceptable for human consumption. Acceptable fowl include chicken, turkey, duck, geese, and pheasant. Unacceptable fowl primarily include the birds of prey - eagles, vultures, owls, and hawks.

Today there is much controversy concerning God's dietary laws. Many New Testament Christians believe they are free to ignore God's instructions of the Old Testament. Many Christians believe that Jesus abolished the dietary laws. The controversy of this issue has led many Christians to become "buffet style Christians." By this I mean they pick and choose which of God's commands to obey, to best suit their desired lifestyle.

Let's look at the Bible, compare the Old and New Testament and conclude as to whether God's dietary laws are applicable today. Answer the following questions:

1. Were the dietary laws, as written in the Bible, man-made traditions, or were they commandments of God? The Bible tells us in Leviticus 11 and Deuteronomy 14 that these dietary instructions were specifically commands of God.

2. Does God expect us to obey His commands? Absolutely! Throughout the Bible, both Old and New Testament, we are instructed to obey God's commands.

3. Does God change His mind? No! Malachi 3:6 says "I am the LORD, and I do not change." Therefore, it seems unlikely that God would make commands in the Old Testament and abolish them in the New Testament without good reason.

4. Was it the intention of Jesus to abolish any of God's laws? No! Matthew 5:17 tells us "Don't misunderstand why I have come. I did not come to abolish the law of Moses or the writings of the prophets. No, I came to fulfill them."

5. Did Jesus obey God's commands? Yes! Jesus obeyed all of God's commands, even the dietary laws. 1Peter 1:19 describes Jesus as the sinless, spotless Lamb of God.

6. Did Jesus teach his disciples to obey or disobey God's commands? Obey! Matthew 5:18 says "I assure you, until heaven and earth disappear, even the smallest detail of God's law will remain until its purpose is achieved." Anybody claiming to be a Christian is to live a Christ-like life. Since Jesus was without sin, obeying all of God's commands, you are to do likewise.

7. Is there a still a need to follow God's dietary laws today? Yes! The plants and animals of the Old Testament are the same plants and animals of the New Testament. The nutritional requirements of the human body of the Old Testament are the same as the nutritional requirements for people today under the New Testament. The dietary laws of the Old Testament were not given to pose a hardship. God gave us these laws to instruct us on how to live a long, healthy life.

8. Is the Old Testament relevant today? Yes! Is the New Testament complete without the Old Testament and vice versa? No! The Old and New Testaments complement one another to give us a complete story. The Old Testament tells us who we are and where we came from. It tells us of God's love and instructs us on how to live. It teaches us about sin, the evil one, and separation from God. It tells us of the prophecy to come. Whereas, the New Testament is the fulfillment of the prophecy. It is the story of God's grace, hope for the future, eternal life, the end of the world, and the ultimate destruction of the evil one. The point I am making here is that the Old Testament is still relevant today.

You cannot live by one testament, either old or new, and realize how much God loves you and fully understand what life is all about.

9. Does modern day science validate God's dietary laws? Yes! Modern science tells us that the meats unfit for human consumption in God's dietary laws are toxic, harmful to the body and detrimental to good health.

There are several New Testament passages which can give the impression that God did, indeed, abolish the dietary commandments which He established in the Old Testament. However, a close look at these passages reveals that they really prove no such thing. The only way a person can use any of these passages to "prove" the nullifying of the dietary laws is to: 1) ignore the context of the passage; 2) ignore the historical background of the passage; 3) ignore what the rest of the Bible says about the subject; 4) ignore the implications and logical conclusions of this theological position.

The first passages to consider is Matthew 15:11, 17-18. "Not what goes into the mouth defiles a man; but what comes out of the mouth, this defiles a man." ... Do you not yet understand that whatever enters the mouth goes into the stomach and is eliminated? But those things which proceed out of the mouth come from the heart, and they defile a man.

The controversy in this chapter is not about clean and unclean foods. The controversy is between God's commandments and man's traditions. The controversy was initiated when the scribes and Pharisees criticized Jesus' disciples for eating with unwashed hands. The Pharisees believed that *Shibia,* an evil spirit, sat upon the hands at night, and this spirit had to be washed off before eating.

These beliefs are rooted in the traditions of men, not in the commandments of God. When Jesus made His statements that some interpret as "declaring all foods clean," He was simply saying that food does not become unclean if it is eaten with unwashed hands. He was simply disagreeing with the tradition that "whoever eats bread without washing his hands is eating unclean bread." His final statement in Matthew 15:20, makes it clear that this was the point He was making: " . . . but to eat with unwashed hands does not defile a man."

Mark 7 also gives an account of this controversy between Jesus and the Pharisees of not washing your hands before eating. In Mark 7:19, the NIV adds ("In saying this, Jesus declared all foods "clean") and the NASB says ("Thus He declared all foods clean").

What most Christians do not know is that this parenthetic interpretation of Jesus' words does not exist in the *Textus Receptus,* the "Received Text" that was accepted by the Church as the only authoritative Greek New Testament text until about a hundred years ago. This parenthetic interpretation of Jesus' words was probably a comment that some scribe wrote in the margin of the text. Later scribes accidentally or deliberately incorporated the marginal comment into the text itself, so the statement appears only in corrupted texts. But the statement does not appear in the *Textus Receptus*, so the KJV says nothing about Jesus "declaring all foods clean."

The passages of Acts 10 tells about Peter's vision of a great sheet descending from heaven. The sheet is filled with unclean animals, and a voice says, "Rise, Peter; kill and eat." Peter says, "Not so, Lord; for I have never eaten anything that is common or unclean."

This vision occurred many years after the Crucifixion and Resurrection. If Jesus had "declared all foods clean" several years earlier, Peter certainly didn't know anything about it! Yet many Christians believe that God sent this vision to tell Peter that He had "changed His mind" about the dietary laws, and abolished them. However, the context shows that the vision had nothing at all to do with a change in God's dietary laws.

As with the earlier hand washing example, the "law" against a Jew entering a gentile's home was not one of God's laws but rather was one of the traditions of the Pharisees. Sadly, Peter had been observing this tradition. He finally understood that Jesus had died to cleanse all of humanity from sin (1 John 1:7, Ephesians 2:14). He could no longer restrict his ministry to Jewish people only. Peter now embraced the knowledge that he could not regard all non-believing gentiles as unclean or believing gentiles as defiled anymore. Jesus did not die to cleanse unclean animals. The unclean animals were only used as symbols in the vision to reveal to Peter how terrible his attitude towards non-Jews was at that time.

Colossians 2:16 says "Therefore do not let anyone judge you by what you eat or drink, ..." Does this mean that Christians are free to eat and drink whatever or as much as they wish? Doesn't the Bible condemn gluttony and drunkenness as well as eating meats not fit for human consumption?

Again we must look at the context of this statement to understand its intended meaning. Colossians 2 also portrays a conflict between man's regulations and God's commands. Verse 8 tells us not to be held captive by following man-made traditions and regulations. Verses 13-15 remind us that we were cleansed and forgiven of our sins through Christ. We are alive in Christ and should follow God's commands, not man's traditions and regulations.

For that reason ["therefore"], *don't give anyone the opportunity to condemn you* ["let no man judge you"] in meat, or in drink, or in respect of a holy day, or the new moon, or the Sabbath days. In other words, through Jesus, you have the power to obey the commandments of God which regulate these things. Therefore, walk in obedience so that no man can condemn you *for not obeying* God's commandments regarding food, drink, holy days, new moon, and Sabbaths.

In 1 Timothy 4:4, Paul tells Timothy "For everything God created is good, and nothing is to be rejected if it is received with thanksgiving." Does this passage tell us to disregard God's dietary laws? You may come to this conclusion if you ignore an important qualifying phrase in verse 3. The qualifying phrase is "which God created to be received." God created specific foods outlined in His dietary laws to be received as food. So, nothing that God created to be used as food need be rejected.

Luke 10:8 says ". . . . eat what is set before you." Does this literally mean you can eat anything, ignoring God's dietary laws? Only if you take this one verse out of context. Luke, Chapter 10 explains that Jesus sent out seventy-two Torah-observant Jews as disciples to spread His teachings. In Matthew 10:6, Jesus tells His disciples not to bother with the Gentiles, rather, look for the lost sheep of the house of Israel (Jews).

It is obvious from these passages that the disciples would be lodging in Torah-observant Jewish homes, where the kosher laws were followed. It is ridiculous to suppose that the disciples might have been offered unclean food in one of these Jewish homes. Even if this very unlikely possibility had occurred, the disciples would have had enough sense to know that this is not what their Master meant when He said to, "eat such things as are set before you." He simply meant to be content with the food that your host provided.

In 1 Corinthians 10:25 Paul instructs Christians to "Eat anything sold in the meat market without raising questions of conscience." Did he literally mean that you could eat any meat? In this case, Paul was telling Christians how to deal with a concern over buying meat in the local markets that may have been sacrificed to idols. God forbids eating meats that were sacrificed to idols, even if it is one of God's approved meats. Paul told the Corinthians that a person was guilty of eating meat offered to idols *only if he knew* that the meat had been offered to an idol. So, don't ask!

Likewise in 1 Corinthians 10:27 Paul instructs Christians to ". . . eat whatever is put before you without raising questions of conscience." This passage does not allow you to eat any meat. It also deals with the concern of eating meat offered to idols. If the meat is fit for human consumption and you don't know that it was sacrificed to idols, it's acceptable to eat.

God's dietary laws of the Old Testament are still applicable today. There is absolutely no scripture in the New Testament that abolishes these dietary regulations. Obedience of God's laws brings life, health, and longevity. Disobedience to God's laws brings sickness, disease, suffering, pain, anguish, sorrow and death.

Biblical Classification of Meats

Meats For Human Consumption		Meats Not For Human Consumption	
Cattle (Beef)	Duck	Pig (Pork)	Shark
Sheep	Goose	Cat	Lobster
Goat	Pheasant	Dog	Crayfish
Buffalo	Quail	Horse	Shrimp
Deer	Dove	Camel	Shellfish
Antelope	Grasshoppers	Fox	Eagles
Fish (with scales and fins)	Crickets	Llama	Hawks
Chicken	Locusts	Rabbit	Vultures
Turkey		Mouse	Ostrich
		Rats	Emu
		Lion	All Amphibians
		Tiger	All Reptiles
		Catfish	

Table 8-1

How you nourish your body plays a major role in your health, your outlook on life, and your personal relationship with God. God has created your body, a temple of God, with specific nourishment requirements. It is your responsibility to be obedient and follow God's plan to nourish your body. We are to eat God's nutritious food that he provided for us, not the toxic, artificially manufactured, nutrient depleted food that man creates.

The Standard American Diet (SAD) is truly sad. It consists of toxic, nutrient depleted foods high in fat, sugar, salt, food additives, and preservatives. Man's ways always lead to destruction, decay, and death. Are you on this path of destruction? Does this sound hopeless? I have good news for you - there is hope.

There is a way that you can enjoy new life, vigor and health. It's God's way! Make the decision right now to make a change in your life. Turn away from man's ways and turn to God. Eat and drink the foods that God specifically designed for you and ignore man's foods. Pause a minute and ask God right now for the courage and strength to make this change in your life. You will be happy you did!

> So whether you eat or drink or whatever you do, do it all for the glory of God.
> **1 Corinthians 10:31 (New International Version, NIV)**

CHAPTER 9

Exercise

Exercise is physical activity to develop or maintain fitness or good health. If we dissect this definition of exercise, we find that the key word of exercise is *activity*. From the physical body perspective activity refers to movement. The body must be placed in motion for exercise to occur. Since most of us live a very hectic and busy lifestyle, does this mean we get plenty of exercise? No, not at all. We are often very busy but do not get much physical activity that develops or maintains fitness or good health. Many of us go to work and sit at a desk for 8 hours a day, sit in our cars driving to and from work and then sit or lay on our couch at home watching television for most of the evening. The average American does not get enough physical activity on a regular basis to promote good health. In fact, our current generation of children is the most unfit, the most overweight, and the most unhealthy generation of children the United States has ever seen.

Technology has played a major role over the last century in changing our lifestyle. Advances in technology have changed our active lifestyle to a sedentary lifestyle. Along with the lifestyle change came an attitude change. We now have the attitude that physical labor is demeaning. Why labor if we can push a button and have technology do something for us? This attitude and lifestyle change reduced our amount of physical activity causing an explosion of overweight and unhealthy Americans by the end of the twentieth century.

What is your attitude toward exercise? I always look forward to my exercise time. I find exercise fun and exhilarating. On the other hand, I know others who get faint just thinking about exercise. Statistics show that only about 37 percent of American adults participate in regular exercise three to five times per week for at least twenty minutes. Approximately 38 percent of adults exercise occasionally and 25 percent of adults do not exercise at all. Whether you love it, hate it, or you are undecided on how you feel about it, regular exercise should be a part of your daily life. Physical exercise is a necessity for all children and adults. It does not matter whether you are 8 or 80 you need to have a regular exercise program.

Why should you exercise? There are many reasons why you should exercise, but the most basic, most compelling reason to exercise is because God demands it! What? You say I cannot find a passage anywhere in the Bible where God says I must EXERCISE! Sure, in 1Timothy 4:8 Paul says physical exercise has some value, but where does God demand it? If you go back to the creation of man in the book of Genesis you will find your answer. After man and women had fallen to sin, God condemned them to work and sweat and labor by working the earth for their food and provisions. Due to Adam and Eve's sin in the Garden of Eden, their lives were changed from one of constant pleasure to one of sweat and physical labor. All of mankind since Adam and Eve also bear this life of physical labor. Physical labor equates to physical activity, and physical activity equates to most of us as exercise.

God has designed your body for physical labor. We have learned from God's natural laws that physical activity is a requirement for good health. One of God's natural principles not directly stated in the Bible, but revealed to man through observation and research is His "Use it or lose it principle." If you do not make good use of what God gives you, He will take it away from you. A good example of this principle is if you do not adequately exercise your muscles, your strength will fade and your muscles will wither away. The scientific word to describe this wasting process is atrophy. If you do not use your strength, you will lose it. If you do not work at maintaining your health you will lose it. That is God's rule.

A century ago, there was still an ample amount of physical labor in our lifestyles. But because of the Industrial Revolution starting in the early 1900s and advances in technology and new inventions, labor performed by Americans became less physical. Urbanization occurred, people moved from rural areas into cities to find work and a perceived better way of life. We have come to a point in time when most of us do very little if any physical labor. Following man's wisdom has allowed us to escape from God's condemnation of a lifetime of physical labor. Or has it? Not really, those that choose not to labor are suffering from their disobedience. Those that choose not to fulfill the physical requirements that God established are paying for it with less than optimal health. You must fulfill God's physical requirements for good health. This is why having a regular exercise program is so important.

What can a regular exercise program do for you? A regular exercise program can work wonders for your health, appearance, attitude, energy level, self-confidence and much more. Table 9-1 lists many benefits that you may receive from regular exercise.

Benefits of Regular Exercise

1. Reduces the risk of premature death
2. Reduces the risk of heart disease by improving blood circulation throughout the body
3. Increases metabolism which helps keep body weight under control
4. Improves blood cholesterol levels
5. Prevents and manages high blood pressure
6. Prevents bone loss
7. Boosts energy level
8. Helps manage stress
9. Releases tension
10. Improves the ability to fall asleep quickly and quality of sleep
11. Improves self-image and confidence
12. Counters anxiety and depression and increases enthusiasm and optimism
13. Increases muscular strength
14. Helps delay or prevent chronic illnesses and diseases associated with aging and maintains quality of life and independence longer

Table 9-1

Benefits of Regular Exercise continued
15. Reduces the risk of developing diabetes
16. Promotes psychological well-being
17. Helps build and maintain healthy bones, muscles, and joints
18. Reduces the risk of developing cancer
19. Increases the amount of oxygen circulating throughout the body
20. Improves flexibility
21. Increases your stamina to do continuous work
22. Improves balance and coordination
23. Reduces the risk of low back problems

Table 9-1

Fitness

In the beginning of this chapter, I told you that exercise is physical activity to develop or maintain fitness or good health. What is fitness? Fitness is defined as good health or physical condition, especially as the result of exercise and proper nutrition. There are five components of fitness that determine your level of fitness:

1. Aerobic Endurance
2. Muscular Strength
3. Muscular Endurance
4. Flexibility
5. Body Composition

Your level of achievement in each of these areas determines your overall level of fitness.

Aerobic Endurance is the ability of your body to sustain an activity for an extended period utilizing aerobic energy. Aerobic literally means "with oxygen." Aerobic exercise is great for increasing the capability of the lungs, heart, blood vessels, and increasing the amount of oxygen transported throughout the body. Some of the benefits of regular aerobic exercise are reduced blood pressure, decreased cholesterol levels, decreases body fat stores, increased heart function, and increased energy levels.

Primary aerobic activities include walking, jogging, running, swimming, cycling, stair climbing, cross country skiing, rowing, rollerblading, and aerobic dance. Secondary aerobic activities include basketball, tennis, racquetball, and soccer.

Muscular Strength is the capacity of your muscles to generate extreme amounts of force in a short period of time utilizing anaerobic energy. Anaerobic literally means "without oxygen." Muscular strength is best described as the maximum amount of weight a person can lift or move. Some of the benefits of regular muscular strength exercise include an increase in physical capacity to do work, improved physical appearance, increased metabolism, decrease in body fat, and decreased risk of injury. The primary activity to increase muscular strength is strength training with free weights and machines using relatively heavy weights and low repetitions.

Muscular Endurance is the ability of a muscle or muscle group to do repeated work over a period of time. Muscular endurance is the ability to exert your strength continuously and repetitively. Muscular endurance is closely related to muscular strength. Muscular endurance is the application of raw strength. A baseball batter needs strength to hit a home run, but a baseball pitcher needs endurance to throw 120 pitches in a baseball game without getting fatigued. Primary activities for developing muscular endurance are free weights and machines using relatively moderate weights with high repetitions (12-15) or calisthenics like sit-ups, pull-ups, and push-ups.

Flexibility is the movement of a joint through the full range of motion. This includes your ability to stretch your muscles and the tendons and ligaments that connect to the bones. Flexibility is important for increased physical efficiency and performance. Some of the benefits of flexibility are decreased risk of injury, increased blood supply and nutrients to joint structure, and increased quality and quantity of joint synovial fluid. Synovial fluid is the fluid that lubricates your joints. As a result of regular flexibility exercise, reflex action is quicker, there is reduced muscular soreness, and a reduced risk of low back pain.

Flexibility is developed and maintained through stretching exercises. A simple example of a stretching exercise is touching your toes while standing and holding this position for 15 to 30 seconds. This exercise stretches the lower back, the back of your thigh, and the calves. Flexibility exercise is part of a complete exercise program and should be done in conjunction with aerobic endurance, muscular strength and muscular endurance exercises during warm-up and cool-down periods.

Body Composition is a technical term used to describe the different components that make up a person's body weight. Body composition analysis identifies the proportion of your body composed of fat versus the proportion of your body composed of lean body tissue. Body fat composition is of primary health concern. People that carry excess body fat are more prone to illness and disease than people who maintain lean body tissue. Obesity has been linked to several diseases such as heart disease, diabetes, stroke, and cancer. Table 9-2 lists body fat composition for different categories of people.

Body Fat Composition Analysis

Category	Athletic	Healthy	Unhealthy	Obese
Men	5 to 13 Percent	12 to 18 Percent	19 to 25 Percent	> 25 Percent
Women	10 to 18 Percent	16 to 25 Percent	26 to 31 Percent	> 31 Percent

Table 9-2

There are several different techniques for obtaining your body fat analysis. A few of the most commonly used techniques for measuring body fat are hydrostatic weighing, Body Mass Index (BMI), skin fold measurements, and Bioelectrical Impedance Analysis (BIA).

The most accurate, somewhat uncomfortable, and the most costly method of analyzing body fat composition is the hydrostatic weighing technique. This method consists of a large tank of water that requires you to be lowered on a chair into the water until you are completely submerged. Hydrostatic weighing is based on Archimedes' principle whereby a submerged object is acted on by a force equal to the volume of water it displaces. In other words, body fat is less dense than water, so fat floats. The difference between your weight on dry land and your weight in the tank is the weight of your body fat.

The body mass index (BMI) expresses the relationship between a person's weight and height. The body mass index is calculated as weight in kilograms, divided by height in meters squared:

$$weight(kg)/height(meters)^2$$

The BMI does not calculate body fat. BMI is a calculation that gives you an indication as to whether you are overweight. The acceptable range is 20-25. Obesity is taken to start at a BMI of 30 and gross obesity at 40. A BMI of 18-20 is defined as mild starvation and severe starvation begins when BMI falls below 16. Here is an example of how to calculate your BMI:

Multiply your weight (in pounds) by 704.5.
Multiply your height (in inches) by your height (in inches).
Divide the first result by the second.

Example: If you're 5'5" and weigh 140:
140 x 704.5 = 98,630
65 x 65 = 4,225
98,630 divided by 4,225 = 23

A major flaw of the BMI is that the calculation does not make any distinction between fat and lean tissue. An athletic person with considerable lean muscle and low body fat could receive a BMI in the overweight classification. Your author is a good example. I am currently at 12 percent body fat and my BMI tells me that I am too fat! The BMI is very popular because it is so easy to calculate, but keep in mind that this index is not a reliable indicator for defining overweight people.

Using skin fold measurements to determine percent body fat is a convenient, less taxing method than hydrostatic weighing. The principle underlying this technique is that approximately half of your fat tissue is subcutaneous (beneath the skin) and is proportional to the total amount of body fat. Using pressure calipers, specific sites on the body are measured. For women, hip, thigh and triceps are measured; for men the chest, abdomen and thigh are measured. The margin of error for skin fold measurements is higher than with hydrostatic weighing. Although a well-trained technician can obtain results that approach the precision of underwater weighing. This is a popular body fat composition analysis because of its convenience, reasonable accuracy and cost.

Bioelectrical impedance analysis (BIA) is a method which uses a small electric current that passes through the body to measure the resistance encountered. Simply explained, BIA measures the impedance or resistance to the signal as it travels through the water that is found in muscle and fat. The more muscle a person has, the more water their body can hold. The greater the amount of water in a person's body, the easier it is for the current to pass through it. The more fat, the more resistance to the current. BIA is safe and it does not hurt. Since BIA emits an electrical current, do not use BIA if you have a pacemaker, or other implanted medical device. The BIA method for body fat composition is also popular because of its convenience, reasonable accuracy and cost.

No matter which method of body fat analysis you choose, none of them are totally accurate. There is some margin of error with all methods. Once you pick a method for measuring body fat composition, stick with it. Track your measurements and follow your trends over time.

Periodically testing your level of fitness in the areas of aerobic endurance, muscular strength, muscular endurance, flexibility, and body composition will allow you to evaluate your overall level of fitness. Testing will indicate which components of fitness are strong and which components are weak. Thus, allowing you to make modifications to your exercise program to improve weak components.

Excuses

About 63 percent of Americans do not get enough regular exercise to keep themselves in good health and physical condition. Among non-exercisers, excuses run rampant. Many of you let unfounded excuses keep you from exercising. Ultimately, leading to an unhealthy lifestyle. Here are some of the more common excuses:

1. **I don't have time to exercise.** It's not a matter of time, it's

a matter of priority! Reprioritize your daily activities placing exercise near the top of your list. Schedule a time to exercise and stick with it.

2. **I'm too old to exercise.** You are never too old to exercise! Exercise can actually delay or prevent many of the degenerative problems of aging like loss of strength and stamina.
3. **I'm already thin.** Being thin is not a good indicator of health or fitness. Thin people need to exercise just like everybody else.
4. **It's too hot or it's too cold.** Depending on where you live there may be times when the outdoor temperatures are too hot or too cold to exercise. If this occurs, either move your exercise session indoors or change the time of day that you exercise. If the summer afternoons are too hot, exercise early in the morning or later in the evening.
5. **I'm too tired.** Exercising will actually increase your energy level! Sounds strange, but exercising will boost your metabolism, oxygenate your blood, and promote proper functioning of your body. On the other hand, not exercising will zap your energy levels.

There are many more excuses that people use to talk themselves out of exercising. Very few excuses have any merit. Severe illness or injury and death are the only valid excuses. Make a commitment to start and continue an exercise program. Your health depends on it.

Exercise Tips

Here are some exercise tips to help you safely get started, stay focused, and maintain your exercise program for a lifetime.

- If you are over 35 years of age and have been sedentary for more than a year or have known medical conditions, consult your health care professional for medical clearance before starting an exercise program.
- When starting a new exercise program start easy and gradually increase intensity over time.
- If you are unfamiliar with setting up an exercise program, consult with a personal trainer.
- Make exercising a priority.

- Schedule your exercise sessions.
- Keep your exercise appointments.
- If you lack the discipline to keep your exercise appointments, workout with an exercise partner and help each other stay committed to keeping your exercise appointments.
- If you find yourself getting bored with your current exercise program. Change it!
- Set realistic goals.
- Pick activities that are enjoyable.

Participating in a lifelong exercise program is absolutely necessary to maintain optimum health and peak physical condition. Americans are overweight, tired, and unhealthy in part due to their disobedience of this directive. It is never too late to start an exercise program. Benefits from exercise are recognized at any age. No matter what your current health condition, I want to encourage you that there is hope. Along with good nutrition, exercise will keep you on the road to optimum health. Ask God for help. Ask Him right now for the courage and strength to get off your couch or out from behind your desk and start an exercise program today.

> O LORD my God, I cried out to you for help, and you restored my health.
> **Proverbs 4:20-22 (The New Living Translation)**

CHAPTER 10

Sleep

Did you get enough sleep last night? If not, you are not alone. More than 100 million people in the United States do not get a good night's sleep on a regular basis. With our hectic and busy lifestyles, sleep often gets shortchanged both in quality and quantity. When it comes to sleep, most people do not realize how important sleep is for proper functioning of the mind and body. The goal of this chapter is to increase your awareness about sleep and to help you understand that sleep is not a luxury, but a necessity. Sleep is a necessity for your happiness, health, and vitality.

What is Sleep?

Sleep is a required natural periodic suspension of consciousness during which the powers of the body are restored.

Sleep Requirements

About one third of your life is spent sleeping. Sleep requirements change over your lifetime. Newborn babies have the greatest sleep requirements, sleeping form 16 to 18 hours per day over six to seven short periods. Sleep requirements gradually decrease with age and stabilize at adulthood. A one-year-old infant requires 14 to 15 hours of sleep per day. A four-year-old child requires about 11 hours of sleep and a ten-year-old child requires about 10 hours of sleep per night. Teenagers require about 9 hours of sleep and adults require 7 to 8 hours of sleep per night.

These sleep requirements are not cast in stone and may vary slightly depending on individual needs. For instance, most adults require 7 to 8 hours of sleep, but some individuals may need a little more sleep such as 9 or 10 hours when recovering from illness or sleep deprivation. Only **you** know the exact amount of sleep you need. If you think you can lead a healthy life receiving less than 7 hours of sleep per night, you are only kidding yourself. Sleep deprivation (lack of sleep) will eventually catch up with you causing illness or even a life threatening accident.

Studies conducted by the American Cancer Society, Finnish researchers and others indicate that people who sleep eight hours per day have the greatest longevity. Those that sleep less than five hours or greater than nine hours have the greatest mortality rate.

Sleep Requirements By Age	
Age Group	**Sleep Requirement (Hours/Day)**
Newborn Baby	16 to 18 (Over 6-7 Periods)
One Year	14 to 15
Four Year	11
Ten Year	10
Sixteen Year	9
Adult	7 to 8

Table 10-1

Stages of Sleep

Sleeping is a lot more complicated than it looks. Researchers have found that sleep occurs in five stages. There are two basic categories of sleep – rapid eye movement (REM) and non-REM. Non-REM sleep is further divided into four stages.

Stage 1 - This first stage of sleep lasts for about 5 to 10 minutes. Stage 1 starts a transition from wakefulness to drowsiness. During this stage you become less perceptive to sounds and actions around you. Stage 1 is a very light sleep. The muscles relax, breathing is smooth, but the brain is still very active. Slow rolling eye movement characterizes this period of sleep. Loud noises may still awaken you.

Stage 2 - Your heart rate, breathing, and brain activity begin to slow down. The body temperature decreases. Stage 2 is a light sleep that lasts longer than Stage 1 sleep, and you return to it several times throughout the night. People normally spend about 50 percent of their total sleep time in Stage 2.

Stage 3 - Your heart rate, breathing, and brain activity continue to slow down. Stage 3 is a deeper sleep than Stage 2 sleep. Your muscles relax and your blood pressure gets lower.

Stage 4 - Brain activity is very slow and it is hard to wake up. Stage 4 is the deepest stage of sleep. Sleepwalking may occur during this stage.

REM - The muscles in the body are totally relaxed, eyes move back and forth very quickly, the heart beats faster, blood pressure increases, and brain activity increases to activity similar to when a person is awake. Dreams and nightmares commonly occur in this stage.

Sleep Cycle

The normal sleep cycle alternates between non-REM and REM stages every 90 to 100 minutes. The sleep cycle starts in stage 1 and successively progresses through stages 2, 3, and 4. Then the cycle reverses backward to stage 3, stage 2, and then to the REM stage. This is one complete sleep cycle. There may be four to six cycles over the course of a sleep period.

The first REM period lasts only 10 minutes. Each subsequent REM period gets longer up to about 60 minutes by the end of the sleep period. The first sleep cycle spends 90 minutes in non-REM sleep and 10 minutes in REM sleep. By the final cycle of the sleep period, the non-REM sleep period is shorter and the REM sleep period is longer. A representative final sleep cycle might be 30 minutes in non-REM sleep and 60 minutes in REM sleep.

Sleep cycles also vary by age. Newborn babies spend about 50 percent of their total sleep time in REM sleep, whereas adults only spend about 20 to 25 percent of their total sleep time in REM sleep.

Functions of Sleep

Although no one knows for sure why we sleep, we know from personal experience that sleep is important for our physical and mental health. We have all experienced times when we received less than adequate amounts of sleep. Symptoms of fatigue, lack of focus, irritability, lack of motivation, memory lapses, and possibly even impaired coordination are often prevalent. Studies have shown that sleep is essential for the normal functioning of the immune system and ability to fight disease and sickness. Sleep is also essential for learning and for healthy cell growth.

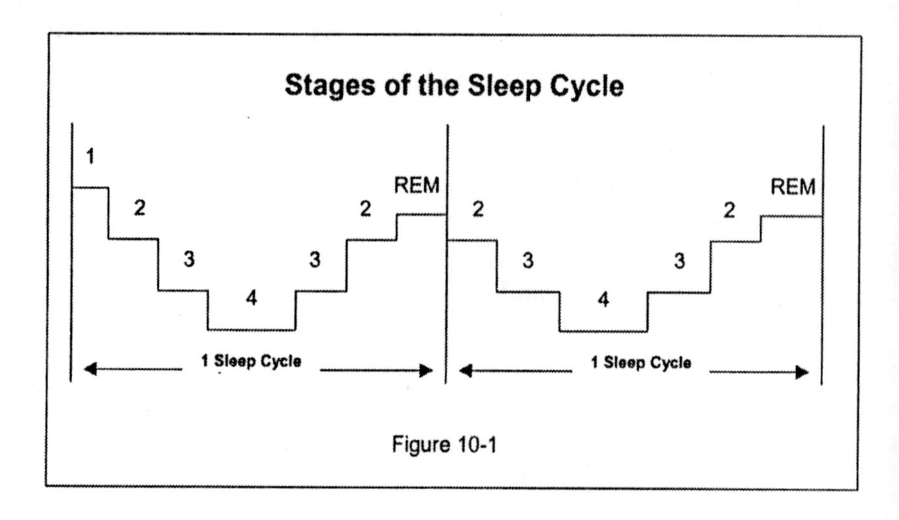

Figure 10-1

There are several theories as to why we sleep:

- Sleep is necessary for revitalizing the brain. The brain uses glucose as its source of energy. When glucose levels in the brain get low they must be replenished. This can only be accomplished during sleep when the brain is inactive. Sleep prepares the brain for the next day and renews our mental balance. Lack of sleep negatively affects our mood and behavior.
- Sleep is crucial for muscle repair. REM sleep completely stops muscle activity and allows the body to repair damaged tissues.
- Sleep is important for healing from illness and trauma. Cell division and repair is faster during sleep. Growth hormone levels, which facilitate growth and repair of body tissues, are highest during sleep.
- Sleep strengthens the immune system. The immune system is highly active during sleep. Levels of immune system molecules interleukin-1 and tumor necrosis factor (TNF) are highest while sleeping. TNF is a potent cancer killer. Lack

of adequate sleep seems to suppress and reduce the overall number of immune cells.

Lifestyle, Sleep and Health

We live in a country that never stops. Work, play, personal and family activities continue around the clock, 24 hours per day, 7 days per week. Adults often push too hard, for too long and suffer the consequences of too little sleep. Consequences like sleepiness, irritability, broken relationships, excessive or more severe illness, mental confusion, and often more accidents or injuries. Sleep deprivation (lack of sleep) continues to be widespread in America. According to the National Sleep Foundation's (NSF) 2001 Sleep in America poll, a majority of adults, 63 percent, do not get the recommended eight hours of sleep needed for good health and optimum performance.

Sleep deprivation impairs memory, reaction time and alertness. Tired people are less productive at work, less patient with others, and less interactive in relationships. Sleep deprivation can also be dangerous. Sleep deprived people are more likely to have accidents. The National Highway Traffic Safety Administration reports that sleepy drivers cause at least 100,000 crashes each year. These crashes result in 40,000 injuries and 1,550 fatalities.

This year's NSF poll also shows that more than one-third of Americans gets less sleep now than five years ago. Americans are working more and sleeping less. Thirty eight percent of respondents work more than fifty hours per week. Those that work more also experience more insomnia (trouble falling asleep) than those who work fewer hours.

Sleep impacts your health and health impacts your quality of sleep. As was noted earlier, sleep deprivation can be a source of physical and mental health problems. Conversely, health problems play a significant role in the quantity and quality of sleep. Health problems are associated with sleep problems such as having trouble falling asleep, staying asleep, waking too early, and waking up feeling non-refreshed or lethargic. Those who report the following medical conditions are most likely to experience a sleep problem: depression (83%), nighttime heartburn (82%), diabetes (81%), cancer (79%), hypertension (79%), heart disease (78%) and/or arthritis (76%).

Unfortunately, sleep deprived parents are teaching their children the same unhealthy sleep habits. Today's kids are overscheduled and overtired. From elementary through high school, kids need nine to eleven hours of sleep each night. But according to the NSF, only 15 percent of kids get 8 ½ or more hours of sleep on school nights. Even more alarming, 25 percent of kids usually sleep 6 ½ hours or less. Tired students don't learn well. Car accidents are more likely to occur for inexperienced teen drivers. Too little sleep can contribute to depression. It is also possible that some children who are labeled ADD or hyperactive are actually acting that way because they are tired.

Not only is the quantity of sleep important, it is important when we sleep. 1 Thessalonians 5:7 says "Night is the time for sleep . . ." God designed your body with a natural biological clock that stimulates sleepiness and wakefulness through chemical processes that are controlled by light and dark. As evening approaches, darkness perceived through your eyes causes the body's temperature to start to drop and stimulates the pineal gland to release the hormone melatonin into our bloodstream. This indicates to your brain and body that it is dark and time to prepare for the transition to sleep. Studies have shown that the urge to sleep for most people builds up throughout the day and peaks around 9 or 10 p.m. Around 4 a.m. your body temperature starts to rise to prepare for wakefulness. Exposure to sunlight each day directs the pineal gland to stop releasing melatonin which signals your brain and body to shift from sleep to wakefulness.

God designed us to work by day and sleep by night. However, our loss of sleep time and natural sleep rhythms can be traced back to a single technological advance – the light bulb. Thomas Edison invented the incandescent bulb in 1879. Although the first incandescent lights were fairly dim, they led to brighter bulbs, such as the tungsten bulbs introduced in the 1910s. Now people could work late into the night. Bright electric lights not only let people stay up longer, but they were also bright enough to mimic the daylight and shift people's internal biological clocks. The incandescent bulb marked the beginning of the modern era of sleeplessness.

Before World War II, few people worked at night. After Pearl Harbor, extremely high production goals required that factory workers produce war materials 24 hours a day, in three eight hour shifts. This was the beginning of shift work that continues today in many professions. Unfortunately, our biological clock is at its lowest ebb in the middle of the night, and people are more prone to distractions, lack of focus, poor memory, bad mood, and slow reaction times often resulting in mistakes. Nearly every major industrial accident in recent decades has occurred after midnight, in the early hours of the morning: the Exxon Valdez grounding, the Chernobyl and Three-Mile Island nuclear accidents, and the Bhopal chemical plant disaster.

Basic Sleep Disorders

The NSF 2001 Sleep in America poll found that 69 percent of respondents experienced frequent sleep problems. Sleep disorders are characterized by disturbances in the amount of sleep, quality or timing of sleep, or in behaviors or physiological conditions associated with sleep. About 70 million Americans suffer from a sleep problem. Sleep problems affect men and women of every age, race, and socioeconomic class. Each year, sleep disorders, sleep deprivation, and sleepiness add an estimated $15.9 billion to the national health care bill. Additional costs to society for such consequences as lost worker productivity and accidents have never been calculated.

There are about 70 different sleep disorders that are generally classified into one of three categories:

- lack of sleep, or insomnia
- disturbed sleep, such as obstructive sleep apnea and
- too much sleep, as with narcolepsy

Insomnia is the inability to fall asleep or remain asleep. It is a common sleep problem that most people at least occasionally experience at various points in their lives. When it occurs, people feel tired much of the time and tend to worry a lot about the fact that they are not getting enough sleep. Consequently, insomnia often disrupts a person's daily life. It can result from emotional difficulties, stress, diet, an underlying disease, and a host of other factors.

Sleep apnea is interrupted breathing during sleep. It can result from malfunctioning neurons, though usually it is a mechanical problem in the windpipe. As people age, their muscle tone relaxes and their windpipe can collapse as a result. Known as obstructive sleep apnea, this causes loud snoring and blocked airflow through the windpipe. A person is unable to breathe for anywhere from 10 to 60 seconds. It may appear that the person is gasping or snorting. Luckily, the brain quickly reacts to the sudden lack of oxygen, the muscles tighten, and the windpipe opens.

Two things happen in a person who suffers from sleep apnea. First, they lose sleep, because every time the windpipe closes, the person has to wake up enough to contract those muscles and resume breathing. As a result, their sleep cycle can be interrupted up to a 100 times a night. Second, every time the windpipe closes, the brain is deprived of oxygen; eventually, this lack of oxygen can cause problems such as morning headaches or a decreased mental functioning. People who have sleep apnea are at a greater risk for heart disease and strokes. A narrowing of the nasal passages or back of the mouth, enlarged tonsils, and obesity are all factors that may contribute to obstructive sleep apnea. Sleep apnea may also be related to the use of alcohol, tobacco, or sedatives.

People with narcolepsy are sleepy during the day and fall asleep uncontrollably throughout the day for periods that last for less than a minute to more than half an hour. These random sleep attacks can occur at anytime, even while the person is engaged in an activity. When they are asleep, narcoleptics have an abnormal sleep pattern. They enter REM sleep prematurely without going through the normal sequence of sleep stages. The symptoms of narcolepsy usually begin sometime between the ages of 15 and 30.

Narcolepsy is usually a genetic disorder, although sometimes it is associated with brain damage or neurological disease. Some people with narcolepsy have noticed that the sleep attacks increase in frequency during certain times, such as pregnancy, illness, fever, or periods of increased stress.

Tips for Healthy Sleep

- Set a Schedule

  Go to bed at a set time each night and get up the same time each morning. Even on weekends. When your sleep cycle has a regular rhythm, you will feel better.

- Do not take naps

  This will insure you are tired at bedtime. If you cannot make it through the day without a nap, sleep less than one hour, before 3 p.m.

- Exercise
  Regular exercise often helps people sleep. Exercise several hours before bedtime. Exercise right before bedtime may be too stimulating and interfere with sleep.

- Do not eat or drink a lot before bedtime
  Drinking too much liquid before bedtime may result in waking up in the night for trips to the bathroom. Do not eat any foods near bedtime that may disrupt your sleep. Avoid all caffeine, alcohol and nicotine products. Eating spicy or fatty foods may cause heartburn and disrupt sleep or prevent you from falling asleep.

- Relax before bed
  A warm bath or shower, reading, or other relaxing routine will help you wind down from a hectic day and make it easier to fall asleep.

- Sleep until sunlight
  If possible, wake up with the sun. Sunlight helps the body's internal biological clock reset itself each day.

- Do not lie in bed awake
  If you cannot sleep, do not just lie there. Do something else like reading or listening to music until you feel tired. The anxiety of being unable to sleep can actually contribute to insomnia.

- Make sure your bed and bedroom are quiet and comfortable
  Maintain a comfortable temperature in the bedroom. Extreme temperatures may disrupt sleep or prevent you from falling asleep. Make sure you have a bed that is comfortable and conforms to your body. An uncomfortable bed can disrupt sleep or prevent you from falling asleep. Keep your bedroom quiet. Silence is more conducive to sleep. If necessary, use earplugs.

- Do not rely on sleeping pills
  Sleeping pills are dangerous drugs that artificially induce sleep but do nothing to treat the cause of your sleeplessness. If necessary use herbal teas or tablets as a sleeping aid until you find and correct the cause of your sleeping problem.

The NSF 2001 Sleep in America poll found that 85 percent of respondents would sleep more if they knew they could be healthier. There is only one way you can be healthier, and by now you know that's God's way. God designed your body with specific sleep requirements for optimum health and vitality. Whether a child or adult, keeping an appropriate sleep schedule is an act of compliance leading to vibrant health. I encourage you to make the effort to adjust your busy lifestyle and develop a daily schedule that allows for adequate sleep for you and your family. God will bless your act of obedience!

> I will never forget your commandments, for you have used them to restore my joy and health.
> **Psalms 119:93 (The New Living Translation)**

Mind

Your brain is a miraculous, complex machine that controls your body functions and allows you to think, reason and experience emotions. God designed your brain with specific requirements for maintaining optimum health. Your brain, being a part of the body, also needs adequate nutrients, mental exercise, and rest. Providing your brain with these necessities leads to good health and optimal mental functioning for a lifetime. Depriving your body of these necessities produces less than optimal health and diminishing mental functioning in your later years of life.

The brain is the portion of your central nervous system that is enclosed within the cranium and composed of gray matter and white matter. It is the primary center for the regulation and control of your bodily activities, receiving and interpreting sensory impulses, and transmitting information to your muscles and body organs. It is also the seat of consciousness, thought, memory, and emotion. This portion of the brain that allows you to think, reason and experience emotions is often referred to as your mind.

There are two schools of thought on the concepts of the brain and the mind. One school believes that the brain and the mind are one in the same, inseparable. The other school feels that the brain and the mind are two separate entities. For the purpose of our discussion this debate is inconsequential.

The first chapter of this section will discuss the basic function and health of the brain. The second chapter will discuss our attitudes, feelings and emotions and how they mold our thoughts and actions.

CHAPTER 11

The Brain

The human brain is a miraculous organ. The brain controls everything the human body does.

It regulates thought, memory, judgement, sensory perceptions, and emotions. It also regulates aspects of the body - including body temperature, blood pressure, heartbeat, and breathing. The brain controls the activities of the body and receives information about the body's inner workings and about the outside world.

A healthy brain allows us to experience, communicate with, and enjoy the world around us. An unhealthy brain often causes us to withdraw inward, sometimes shuts us off from communicating with our outside world, and often robs us of our normal bodily functions. A healthy brain can make life enjoyable and worth living, an unhealthy brain can make life unbearable.

We often take the health and maintenance of our brain for granted until we have problems. Then, it's often too late to repair the damage that has been done to your brain over the years of neglect. Understanding the basics about the brain and how to take care of this unique organ will help you to take the action necessary to improve and maintain your mental power. Following God's ways will significantly increase your chances of enjoying mental power and clarity for a lifetime.

Brain Anatomy and Function

Every component of your body, such as your bones, muscles, skin, and organs, is composed of microscopic cells. This is also true of your brain. The cells of the brain are called neurons. An average brain contains about one hundred billion neurons. In addition to neurons, about nine hundred billion glial cells are present in the brain. These glial cells surround and nutritionally support the neurons.

Brain cells or neurons communicate with each other through electrical impulses and chemicals. These chemicals are referred to as neurotransmitters. Dozens of substances or chemicals in the brain such as amino acids, minerals, and hormones act as neurotransmitters. Table 11-1 gives a brief overview of the major brain chemicals that act as neurotransmitters.

Brief Summary of Major Neurotransmitters

- Acetylcholine helps with memory and learning.
- Dopamine is primarily responsible for mood, alertness, movement, and the ability to experience pleasure and pain.
- Norepinephrine and epinephrine influence alertness, arousal, and mood.
- Serotonin is involved in mood, appetite control, emotional balance, and impulse control.
- GABA (gamma-aminobutyric acid) helps with relaxation and sleep.

Table 11-1

A typical neuron has thousands of connections, called synapses, with neighboring neurons. These synaptic connections allow neurons to communicate with each other by transporting information across the synaptic gap via neurotransmitters. Figure 11-1 is a diagram showing neurons and synapses.

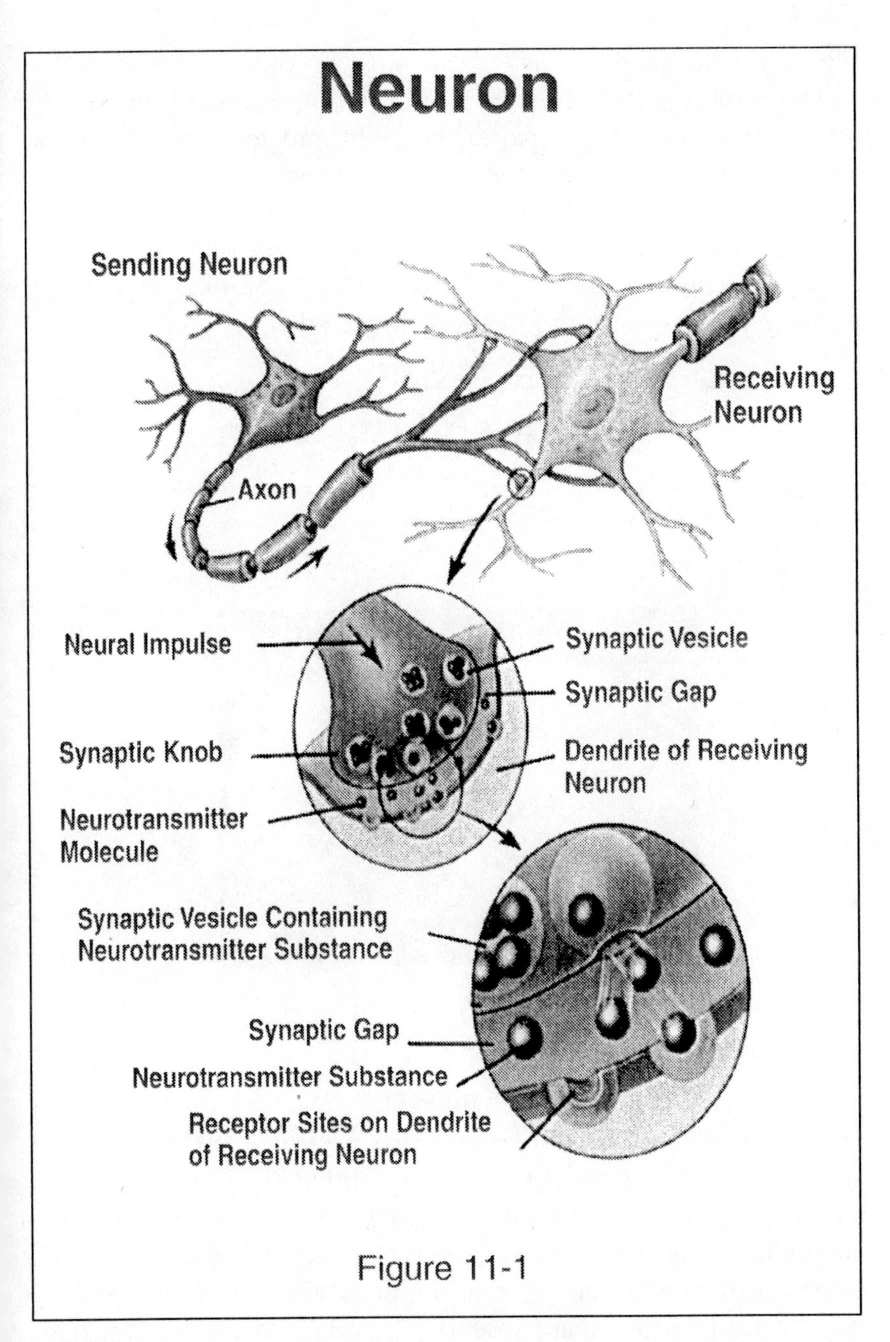

Figure 11-1

The brain of a human adult weighs about 3 pounds. It consists of three major parts: the cerebrum (which makes up the bulk of the brain), the cerebellum located at the back of the brain, and the brain stem which connects the spinal column to the rest of the body (See

Figure 11-2).

The cerebrum, which is the largest portion of the brain, may be divided into two major parts: the right and left cerebral hemispheres. There is a fissure or groove that separates the two hemispheres, called the great longitudinal fissure. The two sides of the brain are joined at the bottom by the corpus callosum. The corpus callosum connects the two halves of the brain and delivers messages from one half of the brain to the other.

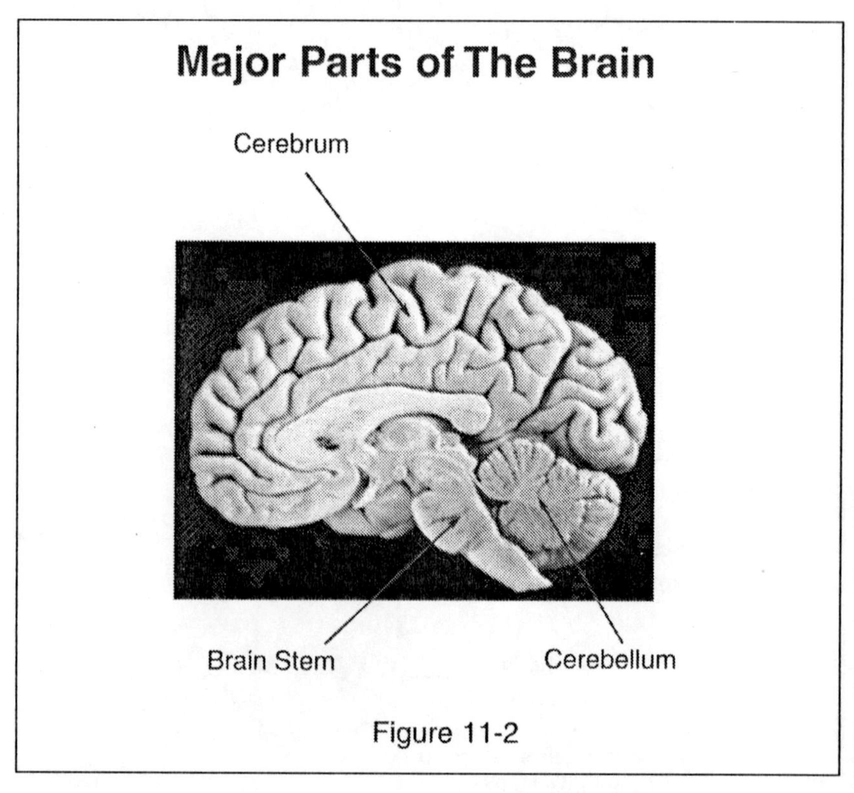

Figure 11-2

The surface of the brain appears wrinkled. The cerebral cortex has small grooves called sulci, larger grooves called fissures and bulges between the grooves called gyri. Scientists have specific names for the bulges and grooves on the surface of our brain. They serve as landmarks and are used to help isolate very specific regions of the brain. Decades of scientific research have revealed the specific functions of the various regions of the brain.

The cerebral hemispheres have several distinct fissures. By finding these landmarks on the surface of a brain, the brain can effectively be divided into "lobes". Lobes are simply broad regions of the brain. The cerebrum or brain may be divided into four lobes: frontal, temporal, parietal and occipital lobes. Each lobe serves very specific functions.

Frontal Lobe	Plays an important part in our intelligence, concentration, temper, personality, problem solving and voluntary movement. It helps us set goals, make plans, set our priorities and guides our head and eye movements.
Temporal	Plays an important part in hearing sounds, memory, language and speech functions.
Parietal	Plays an important part in interpreting our sensory signals received from other parts of the brain and spatial perception. It helps us with orientation and perception of our external world.
Occipital Lobe	Plays an important part in our vision. It helps us see light and objects and allows us to recognize and identify them.

The cerebellum is located at the back of the brain beneath the occipital lobe. The cerebellum fine-tunes our motor activity or movement. It coordinates muscle movement and helps us maintain our posture, our sense of balance or equilibrium by controlling the tone of our muscles and senses the position of our limbs.

The brain stem is located in front of the cerebellum and may be considered as a "stem" or structure holding up the cerebrum. It consists of three structures: the midbrain, pons and medulla oblongata. Many simple or primitive functions that are essential for survival are located here.

The midbrain is an important center for ocular motion while the pons is involved with coordinating the eye and facial movements, facial sensation, hearing and balance. The medulla oblongata controls our breathing, blood pressure, heart rhythms and swallowing. These functions are important to our survival. Messages from the cortex to the spinal cord and nerves that branch from the spinal cord are sent through the pons and the brain stem. Destruction of these regions of the brain will cause "brain death". The heart can no longer beat on its own. Lungs cannot work on their own. Unable to breathe, oxygen will not be delivered to the brain. Brain cells, which require oxygen to survive, will die.

The reticular activating system is found in the midbrain, pons, medulla and part of the thalamus. It controls our level of wakefulness, the attention we pay to what happens in the world that surrounds us, and our pattern of sleep.

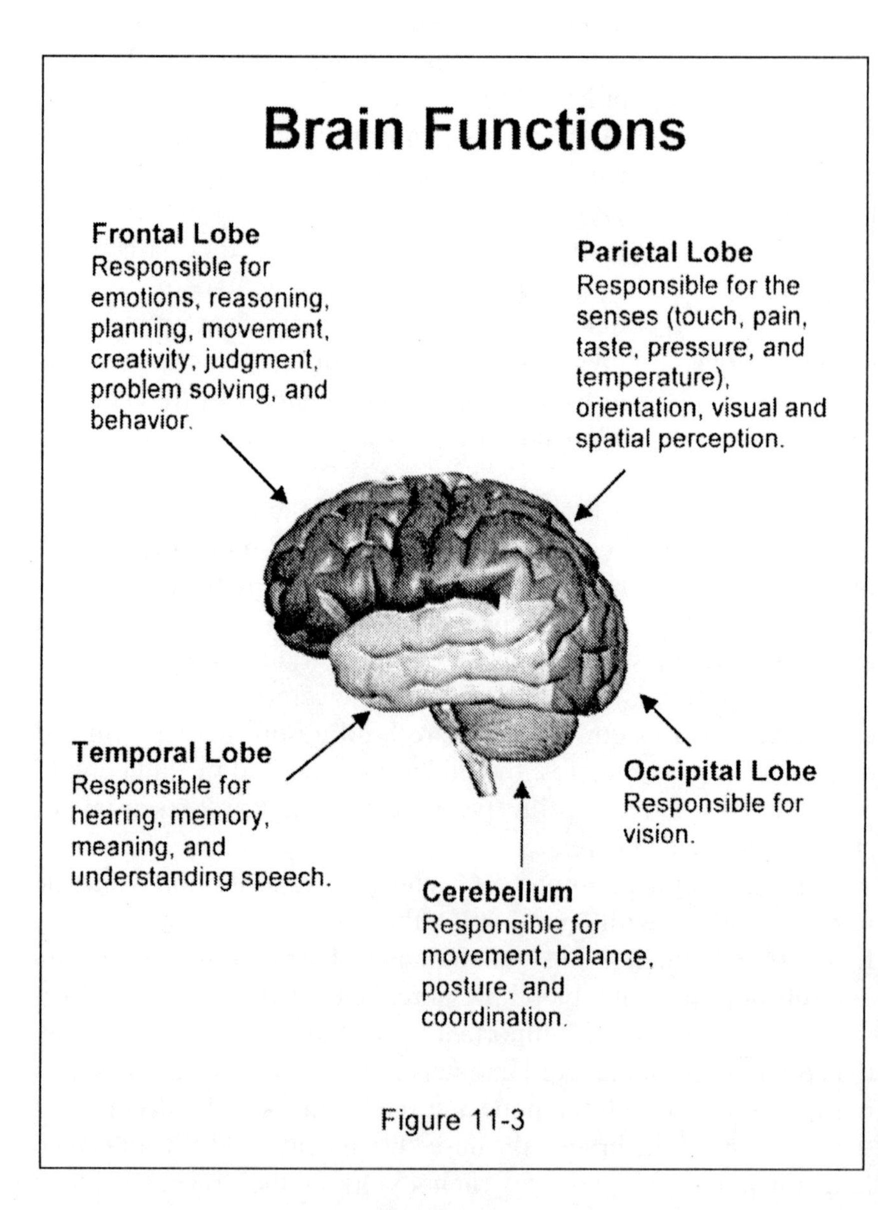

Figure 11-3

Brain Disorders

The human brain is a remarkable organ controlling every function of the body. But it is also subject to many disorders and disease such as Alzheimer's and Parkinson's disease, and depression and schizophrenia. Brain disorders affect millions of people in the United States and has an economic impact of billions of dollars. When diseases or disorders strike the brain, the results can be devastating. Nobody can say for sure what specifically causes any of these brain disorders. I can tell you that God promised to keep you healthy if you are obedient to his ways. As researchers continue to investigate disorders and diseases of the brain, they find that the causes generally point to a few common links: inadequate blood supply, malnutrition, reduced oxygen supply, chemical imbalances, suppressed immunity, and accumulation of toxins.

There are many brain disorders that affect Americans today. Although brain disorders are thought to usually affect the elderly, brain disorders may occur as early as childhood and last a lifetime. The following survey is a listing of the more common brain disorders to give you a better understanding of the causes, cures, and devastating effects these disorders can have on people.

Alzheimer's Disease

Alzheimer's disease (AD) is a neurodegenerative disorder characterized by a progressive decline in memory, judgement and the ability to reason and sustain intellectual function. The cause of AD is unknown, and no cure is available.

The German physician Alois Alzheimer first described AD in 1907. AD is now the most common brain disorder in older people. An estimated 4 million people in the United States suffer from AD.

Early symptoms may include memory loss, difficulty with abstract thinking and disorientation in time and place. The disease usually begins after age 65, and the risk of AD goes up with age. People may have AD anywhere from 5 to 20 years. The most common cause of death in AD patients is infection.

Parkinson's Disease

Parkinson's disease (PD) is a progressive disorder of the central nervous system. Clinically, the disease is characterized by a decrease in spontaneous movements, gait difficulty, postural instability, rigidity and tremor. PD is caused by the degeneration of the pigmented neurons in the Substantia Nigra of the brain, resulting in decreased availability of the neurotransmitter dopamine. The reason for this degeneration is unknown and there is no known cure for PD.

The English physician James Parkinson first described PD in 1817. An estimated 1.5 million people in the United States suffer from PD.

The classic symptoms of PD include resting tremor on one side of the body, generalized slowness of movement, stiffness of limbs (rigidity), and gait or balance problems. Other symptoms may include cramped handwriting, lack of arm swing on the affected side, decreased facial expression, lowered voice volume, feelings of depression or anxiety, slight foot drag on the affected side, increase in dandruff or oily skin, less frequent blinking and swallowing.

PD may occur at any age, but it is uncommon in people younger than 30, and the risk of developing PD increases with age. The symptoms first appear, on average, at about age 60, and the severity of Parkinson's symptoms tends to worsen over time.

Cerebral Palsy

Cerebral palsy (CP) is a broad term used to describe a group of chronic disorders impairing control of movement. The term cerebral refers to the brain's two halves, or hemispheres, and palsy describes any disorder that impairs control of body movement. Thus, these disorders are not caused by problems in the muscles or nerves. Instead, faulty development or damage to motor areas in the brain disrupts the brain's ability to adequately control movement and posture. The cause of CP is unknown and no cure is available.

The English surgeon William Little first described CP in the 1860's. An estimated 500 thousand people in the United States suffer from CP.

CP occurs in babies, possibly in the womb, during delivery or shortly after birth. The symptoms first appear during the first few years of life and do not worsen.

Multiple Sclerosis

Multiple sclerosis (MS) is a chronic, often disabling disease of the central nervous system. MS is an inflammatory demyelinating condition. Myelin is a fatty material that insulates nerves, acting much like the covering of an electric wire and allowing the nerve to transmit its impulses rapidly. It is the speed and efficiency with which these impulses are conducted that permits smooth, rapid and coordinated movements to be performed with little conscious effort. In Multiple Sclerosis, the loss of myelin (demyelination) is accompanied by a disruption in the ability of the nerves to conduct electrical impulses to and from the brain and this produces the various symptoms of MS. The sites where myelin is lost (plaques or lesions) appear as hardened (scar) areas. In MS these scars appear at different times and in different areas of the brain and spinal cord. The term Multiple Sclerosis literally means, many scars. The exact cause is unknown, but there appears to be multiple causes in MS, possibly including viruses and environmental, genetic, and immune system factors. There is no cure available.

MS was first identified by French neurologist Jean-Martin Charcot in 1868. An estimated 250 to 350 thousand people in the United States suffer from MS.

The symptoms of MS are highly variable, depending on the areas of the central nervous system that have been affected. Not only do the symptoms vary from one person to another, but from day to day for any given individual. Symptoms include fatigue, tingling, numbness, painful sensations, blurred or double vision, muscle weakness, impaired balance, spasticity, tremor, changes in bladder, bowel, and sexual function, cognitive changes such as forgetfulness or difficulty concentrating, speech and swallowing problems, and mood swings. Symptoms may come and go, appear in any combination, and be mild, moderate or severe. Some people will experience only a few of these symptoms in the course of their MS, while others will experience many more.

Most people with MS are diagnosed between the ages of 20 and 40 but the unpredictable physical and emotional effects can last a lifetime. MS is rarely diagnosed under 12 and over

55 years of age. The progress, severity and specific symptoms of MS in any one person cannot yet be predicted. Life span is not significantly affected by MS.

Huntington's Disease

Huntington's Disease (HD) is a devastating, degenerative brain disorder that slowly diminishes the affected individual's ability to walk, think, talk and reason. HD is now recognized as one of the more common genetic disorders. There is no cure available.

Dr. George Huntington first described HD in 1872. An estimated 250 thousand people in the United States suffer from HD.

Early symptoms of Huntington's Disease may affect cognitive ability or mobility and include depression, mood swings, forgetfulness, clumsiness, involuntary twitching and lack of coordination. As the disease progresses, concentration and short-term memory diminish and involuntary movements of the head, trunk and limbs increase. Walking, speaking and swallowing abilities deteriorate. Eventually the person is unable to care for him or herself. Death follows from complications such as choking, infection or heart failure.

HD typically begins in mid-life, between the ages of 30 and 45, though onset may occur as early as the age of 2. Children who develop the juvenile form of the disease rarely live to adulthood. HD affects males and females equally and crosses all ethnic and racial boundaries. Each child of a person with HD has a 50-50 chance of inheriting the fatal gene.

Brain Tumors

Brain tumors are abnormal growths found inside the skull. Cells reproducing themselves in an uncontrolled manner cause a tumor. Tumors are classified as benign (non-cancerous) and malignant (cancerous). Benign tumors are generally harmless, but may be life threatening based on their location in the brain. Malignant tumors are life threatening. The cause of brain tumors is unknown.

Brain tumor symptoms are unique, but general statements about symptoms can be made. Some symptoms are due to increased pressure caused by the growing tumor. Other, more specific, symptoms are related to the tumor's location, type, and size.

- Headaches

  Headaches are a common initial symptom and the majority of patients experience headaches sometime during the course of their illness. Typical brain tumor headaches come and go and usually do not throb. They are worse in the morning and improve gradually during the day. They can rouse the person from sleep. These headaches can worsen with coughing, exercise, or with a change in position such as bending or kneeling.

  Headaches are usually due to pressure in the brain. Some people experience neck pain as well.

- Seizures

  Seizures are caused by a disruption in the normal flow of electricity in the brain. Those sudden bursts of electricity can cause a variety of symptoms including convulsions, unusual sensations, and loss of consciousness. Focal seizures can also occur.

  Symptoms of a focal seizure depend upon the tumor's location and can include muscle twitching or jerking, abnormal smells or tastes, problems with speech or numbness and tingling. Seizures are the presenting symptom in approximately one-third of patients. About half of all patients experience some form of seizure during their illness.

- Mental changes

  Mental changes frequently occur. These can range from problems with memory, speech, communication and/or concentration to severe intellectual problems and confusion. Changes in behavior, temperament and personality are other indications of mental change.

  Mental changes are caused directly by the tumor, by increased pressure within the skull or by involvement of the areas of the brain that control personality.

- Mass effect symptoms due to Increased IntraCranial Pressure (IICP)

  IICP is caused by:
  - the tumor's growth within the skull-an area enclosed by bone which cannot expand, and/or
    - hydrocephalus-blockage of the fluid that flows around and through the brain, and/or
    - edema-swelling of the brain around the tumor due to an accumulation of fluid.

These all result in mass effect. Mass effect can cause further damage by compressing and displacing delicate brain tissue.

The symptoms caused by increased intracranial pressure include nausea and vomiting, drowsiness, vision problems such as blurred or double vision or loss of peripheral vision, and the headaches and mental changes already mentioned.

- Focal Symptoms
  In addition to the common, but non-specific symptoms listed above, other more specific symptoms frequently occur. These "focal symptoms" can help identify the location of the tumor. Focal symptoms include: hearing problems such as ringing or buzzing sounds or hearing loss, decreased muscle control, lack of coordination, decreased sensation, weakness or paralysis, difficulty with walking or speech, balance problems, or double vision.

  It is expected that over 180,000 brain tumors will be diagnosed in the United States during 2001. Approximately 2,200 children younger than age 20 are diagnosed annually with brain tumors. About 13,000 people in the United States die of malignant brain tumors each year.

<u>Amyotrophic Lateral Sclerosis</u>

Amyotrophic lateral sclerosis (ALS), often referred to as "Lou Gehrig's disease," is a progressive neurodegenerative disease that attacks nerve cells in the brain and the spinal cord. Motor neurons reach from the brain to the spinal cord and from the spinal cord to the muscles throughout the body. The progressive degeneration of the motor neurons in ALS eventually lead to their death When the motor neurons die, the ability of the brain to initiate and control muscle movement is lost. With all voluntary muscle action affected, patients in the later stages of the disease become totally paralyzed. Yet, through it all, for the vast majority of people, their minds remain unaffected. The cause of ALS is unknown and no cure is available.

ALS was first identified by French neurologist Jean-Martin Charcot in 1869. It is estimated that as many as 30,000 Americans have the disease at any given time. Approximately 5,000 people in the U.S. are diagnosed with ALS each year.

Early symptoms of ALS often include increasing muscle weakness, especially involving the arms and legs, speech, swallowing and breathing. When muscles no longer receive the messages from the motor neurons that they require to function, the muscles begin to atrophy (waste away).

Most people who develop ALS are between the ages of 40 and 70, with an average age of 55 at the time of diagnosis. However, cases of the disease do occur in persons in their twenties and thirties. Generally though, ALS occurs in greater percentages as men and women grow older. The life expectancy of an ALS patient averages about two to five years from the time of diagnosis.

I have only touched on the surface of the more common brain disorders that affect Americans today. You are now aware that brain disorders can afflict both the young and the old, and the affects are sad and devastating. The point I want to make here is that, in some cases, man has spent more than a century researching these brain disorders. Yet, man's wisdom cannot tell you what causes these disorders, how to cure these disorders, or how to prevent these disorders. Only God can!

> He said, "If you listen carefully to the voice of the LORD your God and do what is right in his eyes, if you pay attention to his commands and keep all his decrees, I will not bring on you any of the diseases I brought on the Egyptians, for I am the LORD, who

heals you."
Exodus 15:26 (New International Version, NIV)

Brain Health and Maintenance

There are many simple things that you can do to insure a healthy brain and optimize brain function.

- Feed your brain – proper nourishment is vital.
- Avoid toxins from foods, water, and air. This includes alcohol, caffeine, and nicotine.
- Get adequate sleep – revitalizes your brain.
- Reduce stress and worry – has a negative effect on the brain.
- Physical exercise – increases blood flow and oxygen to the brain, relieves stress.
- Protect your brain from injury by wearing a helmet when riding a bike or motorcycle, roller blading, skate boarding, or skiing. Also wear a helmet at construction sites or anywhere debris could fall on your head. Always wear a seat belt when driving in a vehicle. Wear a helmet when playing sports like football, hockey, and baseball. Do not let children hit soccer balls with their head.
- Modify negative thoughts and attitudes to positive ones. Negative thoughts usually lead to destructive behavior or unfounded fears.
- Exercise your brain – learning is good for you. Learning enhances blood flow and activity in the brain. Remember the "use it or lose it principle."
- Spend time with people you like. Relationships with people you like can be rewarding and energizing.

A healthy, well functioning brain can last a lifetime if you follow God's maintenance requirements. Good health takes time, planning, and effort, but it's well worth it. No matter what your physical or mental condition is today, you can take steps right now to improve your mind and body. Are you ready to make a change in your life and do what is right in God's eyes? Are you wise enough to make the effort and follow God's way?

Therefore everyone who hears these words of mine and puts them into practice is like a wise man who built

his house on the rock. The rain came down, the streams rose, and the winds blew and beat against that house; yet it did not fall, because it had its foundation on the rock. But everyone who hears these words of mine and does not put them into practice is like a foolish man who built his house on sand. The rain came down, the streams rose, and the winds blew and beat against that house, and it fell with a great crash.
Matthew 7:24-27 (New International Version, NIV)

CHAPTER 12

Matters of the Mind

This chapter may be the most important chapter of this book. Why? Because all the other chapters are worthless unless you make up your mind to change your ways and follow God's way to health and happiness.

Your mind is the control center of all your thoughts, emotions, and actions. Your spirit may provide guidance to your mind. Your body will carry out the actions of your mind. But, your mind makes your decisions and ultimately puts them into action or fails to put them into action. Your mind is the center for righteousness and evilness. Your mind controls your joys and fears. Your mind even decides whether you are healthy or sick.

The quality of your thoughts and actions is based upon several different things. What you think, do, and say comes from a compilation of many factors. Your environment is one such factor. Were you raised in a warm, loving, affluent home or were you raised in an alcoholic home where fear, loneliness, brutality, and maybe poverty prevailed? A child raised in a warm loving home will have a different perspective on life than the child raised in the alcoholic home. These children will have different perspectives on life that will mold their character and attitude that may very well last a lifetime.

What you feed your mind is also an important factor in determining the quality of your thoughts and actions. I'm referring to the physical nourishment of the mind as well as the sensory feeding of the mind. Malnutrition, which is prevalent in America today, can lead to unhealthy thinking. For example, schizophrenia, a mental disorder characterized by loss of contact with reality and disintegration of personality, can result from a simple vitamin and mineral deficiency.

What we feed our mind through the sensory perceptions of sight and sound has an impact on our mind as well. What we see and listen to through television, music, books, and the internet has a profound affect on what we think, do, and say. There is no doubt that the negative, violent, sexually oriented material viewed or listened to through these types of media has a negative impact on our thoughts and behavior. Studies conclude that viewers of violent TV content learn aggressive behaviors and attitudes, become desensitized to violence and often become fearful of being victimized.

Another factor that molds our thoughts and actions is our personal experiences. Probably all children are told by their parents not to touch the top of the stove because it is hot. Did you accept your parent's advice and stay away from the stove or did you go and touch the hot stove and burn your finger? If you touched the hot stove, the pain you experienced probably changed your thoughts about touching the hot stove and you never touched it again. Personal experiences impact our thinking.

Negative Thinking

Negative thoughts hold us back from living up to our full potential. Negative thoughts like fear and doubt and "I can't" hold us back from fulfilling our desires and accomplishing God's will for our life. Whatever we think often becomes our reality. I you think you can't learn to play the piano, you'll never learn to play the piano. If you think that you can never be healthy, you'll never be healthy. Negative thinking can lead you to a life of misery and underachievement. The power of the mind became very evident to Job. He found that his thoughts became his reality.

> "What I feared has come upon me; what I dreaded has happened to me. I have no peace, no quietness; I have no rest, but only turmoil."
> **Job 3:25-26 (New International Version, NIV)**

It's amazing how our thoughts control who we are, what we are, and what we do over our lifetime. Satan gloats about keeping us prisoners of our own minds through fears and doubts. It doesn't have to be this way. God's strength, power and confidence can break those chains of bondage and free you forever. Let Godly, positive thoughts permeate your mind. Think "I can" and "I will" and know that God will guide and provide. If you believe you can do something and you visualize yourself accomplishing this endeavor, you shall succeed.

Character

All of these various factors that affect your mind sets the foundation for who you are, your attitudes, and your character. What is character? Character is the combination of mental and ethical traits that distinguishes one person from another. There is good character and bad character. Good character can be defined as "doing what is right and good." Bad character is "doing what is wrong." Who decides what is right and good? Ultimately, God decides what is right and good. God's word written in the Bible teaches us what is right and what is wrong. Without this divine instruction, everyone would have their own interpretation of right and wrong and our country would be in chaos – just like it is today!

What personal traits make up good character? The following traits make up good personal character:

- **Honesty** – Be truthful, sincere, and straightforward.
  Do not lie, cheat, or steal.
  Do not intentionally mislead others.

- **Integrity** – Always do what is right, even when it is costly or difficult.
  Do not compromise your values by giving in to temptation.

- **Reliability** – Follow through on commitments.
  Keep your promise.

- **Respect** – Treat others the way you want to be treated.
  Have consideration for others.

- **Responsibility** – Be accountable for your actions; not making excuses or blaming others.
  Do what needs to be done.
  Finish what you start.

- **Fairness** – Treat people equally and impartially.
  Be open minded and reasonable.

Play by the rules.
Do not take advantage of others.

- **Caring** – Treat others with kindness, concern, and generosity.
Be charitable.
Give of yourself for the benefit of others.

- **Citizenship** – Make our democratic republic work by voicing opinions, voting, and participating in the decision making process.
Perform community service.
Help take care of the environment.
Obey the laws.

Does character matter? Absolutely! God says that character matters. An example of good character was displayed by a young king named Josiah (2 Kings 22). At age 8 he was crowned king of Judah. He had already been taught that God's laws make for a happy and secure life, but he had to make the decision to follow them. The many adults who surrounded and clearly outnumbered him did not obey God's laws. In fact, they were at the other extreme, worshiping idols.

Young Josiah recognized that the citizens of his kingdom would oppose his decisions, but this didn't deter him. He set himself to rid the land of anything that offended God. This approach inspired his people, and they respected the young ruler for standing up for what was right. He showed good character and wasn't ashamed to stand up for godly morals. Josiah eventually became a great king, and God honored him as an example for people down through the ages to follow. The character that made him a truly great leader was formed during his youth.

> When the godly are in authority, the people rejoice. But when the wicked are in power, they groan.
> **Proverbs 29:2 (New Living Translation)**

It seems the common notion that character doesn't matter is prevalent in America today. This notion seems to run rampant in business and politics. Lying, cheating, and immoral deeds don't seem to matter if you have power or produce results. During his second term, President Bill Clinton sexually abused a White House intern, then lied under oath, committing perjury, a crime that deserved impeachment. Not only did President display immoral character, the U.S legislative branch showed their lack of character by refusing to impeach President Clinton for his crime. The moral decline of America continues to spiral downward because society does not demand good character from its citizens.

Good character will make the difference between experiencing a successful life or a life of painful frustrations. Today's world labors under the false premise that good character doesn't count. But the viewpoint of this world is dead wrong. Don't believe everything others think, and don't follow this world's example. Let God take charge of your life, and make character count.

Good character does matter to God and it should matter to you. I encourage you to complete the Character Self-Assessment located in Appendix C.

Attitude

Your attitude plays an important role in your mental and physical well being as well as your success in life. An upbeat, positive attitude can make for a happy, healthy, successful life. A gloomy, negative attitude usually makes for a life of sadness, illness, and defeat. Isn't this an interesting concept? Attitude is merely a state of mind. Why does a state of mind have such a profound impact on your life?

Our state of mind is merely a barometer of how we feel about life. And how we feel about life controls what we think, say, and do. Which person seems most like you in the morning?

> **Person 1**:The alarm clock rings. I get out of bed quickly. I'm excited about the new day. I look forward to going to work. I'm excited about being with my friends and family. I look forward to the opportunities God will bring my way today.
>
> **Person 2**:The alarm clock rings. I hit the snooze alarm. I wonder how the new day got here so quickly. I don't want to get out of bed. The alarm clock rings again. I crawl out of bed. I'm depressed about the new day – work, family obligations, the

whole day is shot. I hope nothing terrible happens to me today!

I hope you are most like Person 1, but unfortunately most people have more in common with Person 2. Person 1 is energetic, optimistic, glad to be alive, and makes things happen. Whereas, Person 2 is tired, pessimistic, wonders why he is still alive, and waits for things to happen to him. Person 1 has a positive attitude and optimistic outlook. Person 2 has a negative attitude and pessimistic outlook. Which person is most likely to be happy, healthy, and successful?

Which person would you prefer to be? Obviously, we all want to be like Person 1. The good news is that you can be like Person 1! Since our attitude is just a state of mind, you can change your attitude.

> "The longer I live the more I realize the impact of attitude on life. Attitude, to me, is more important than facts. It is more important than the past, than education, than money, than circumstances, than failures, than successes, than what other people think or say or do. It is more important than appearance, giftedness, or skill. It will make or break a company… a church… a home. The remarkable thing is we have a choice everyday regarding the attitude we will embrace for that day. We cannot change our past… we cannot change the fact that people will act in a certain way. We cannot change the inevitable. The only thing that we can do is to play on the one string we have and that is our attitude… I am convinced that life is 10% what happens to me and 90% how I react to it. And so it is with you… we are in charge of our attitudes."
>
> —Charles Swindoll

Here are a few tips to help you get started on improving your attitude.

1. **Think like you want to be**
   It's tough to be happy, joyful, successful, etc. if you don't think that you are a happy, joyful, and successful person. You become what you think you are.
2. **Change your environment**
   Make your environment reflect the attitude you wish to have.

If your home or office is dark and dreary, make changes to create a bright, cheery, and uplifting atmosphere.

3. **Follow the example of others**
   Associate with positive, successful people. Learn from their example.
4. **Smile**
   Research has shown the smiling has both psychological and physiological effects. It's difficult to be negative when you have a smile on your face.
5. **Educate yourself**
   Read books, articles, and magazines that help you understand and change your attitude. Educate yourself about new things you've always wanted to learn about.
6. **Change your actions**
   If you do what you've always done, you'll get what you've always gotten. Change your actions and watch your results change.
7. **Help others**
   Helping others will help you. One of the fastest ways to change your attitude is to take the focus off yourself and to help others in need.
8. **Expect the best**
   Always do your best and expect the best.
9. **Study your Bible**
   The Bible is full of stories of people with positive attitudes. Let God's word touch your heart. Read and incorporate these lessons into your life.
10. **Don't give up**
    Change often occurs slowly, over an extended period of time. If you don't get immediate results, don't be surprised and DON'T QUIT, be persistent.

Mind/Body Connection

Have you ever had a pain or illness that could not be explained by your doctor? Maybe someone told you "It's all in your mind." Your problems may very well be all in your mind. Your mind has a very powerful influence over the well being of the body. Positive, optimistic thoughts and positive feelings like love, joy, and contentment promote good health. Negative, pessimistic thoughts and negative feelings like hate, anger, and loneliness promotes illness and decay.

Our thoughts and feelings influence the body via two kinds of mechanisms: the nervous system and the circulatory system. These are the pathways of communication between the brain and the rest of the body.

The brain reaches into the body via the nervous system. This allows it to send nerve impulses into all the body's tissues and influence their behavior. The brain can thus affect the behavior of the immune system, endocrine system, all the bones, muscles, all the internal organs, and even the walls of veins and arteries.

The brain is also a gland. It manufactures thousands of different kinds of chemicals and releases them into the bloodstream. These chemicals circulate throughout the body and influence the activity and behavior of all the body's tissues. The brain could be described as the ultimate pharmacy, producing many more drugs than science has ever invented.

Stress is a major contributor of mind/body related illnesses. Did you know that 60 – 90% of all physician visits are for stress-related complaints. Stress has been linked to all leading causes of death, including heart disease, cancer, stroke, accidents, cirrhosis, and suicide.

What is stress? Stress is a physical, chemical or emotional factor to which an individual fails to make a satisfactory adaptation. Very simply, stress is change. Anything that causes a change in your life causes stress. Stress is merely our reaction to the change. Stress can be the pressure we feel from change or other influences. Stress comes in all shapes and sizes, but all stress is not bad. Stress is an unavoidable consequence of life. Life without stress would be incredibly dull and boring. Life with just the right amount of stress brings out our best performance. Life with too much stress becomes unpleasant, tiring, and unhealthy.

Stress can occur from both external and internal sources. External stress can be the loss of a job, the death of a family member, or conflicts with friends. Internal stress can occur from illness, pain, or even unfounded fears and worry. The fear of flying, the fear of public speaking, or the worries over an ill family member are examples of internal stress. It doesn't matter whether the stress is internal or external. The overall effects are the same.

As you think about stress you may be relating stress to negative changes or bad experiences that occur to you. Negative changes and bad experiences do indeed cause stress, but so do positive changes and good experiences. Getting married is both a positive change and a good experience, but getting ready and preparing for a wedding is very stressful. Bringing a newborn baby into your life is a joyful occasion, yet the changes that occur in your lifestyle and the demands of caring for a newborn are very stressful. Not only does change cause stress, so do agreeable experiences, exciting challenges, and stimulating competition. It doesn't matter whether the stress is good or bad. The overall effects are the same.

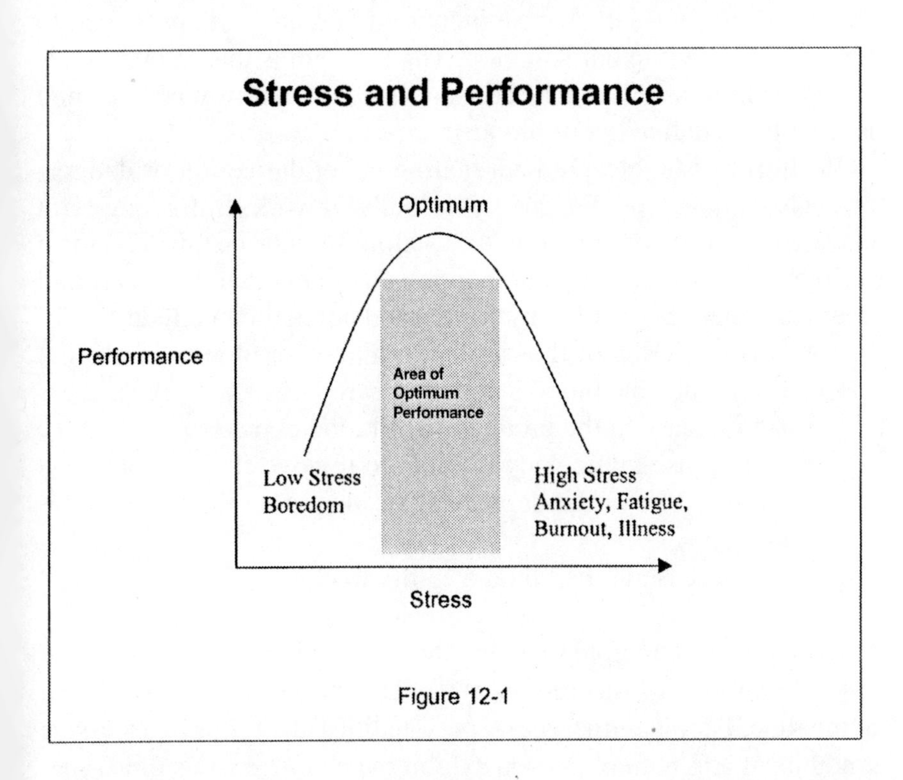

Figure 12-1

Whenever your brain perceives a stimulus such as a change, a challenge, or an emergency it signals your adrenal glands to release stress hormones. The most notable stress hormone being adrenaline. When this state of alarm or emergency is triggered adrenaline is released to physiologically prepare your body to either take on the challenge or run away from it. This is known as your "fight or flight" response. This natural, God given mechanism was designed to help us deal with emergencies. The increase of adrenaline in your bloodstream activates your heart, raises your blood pressure, causes your heart to beat faster, increases your rate of breathing, sends glucose to your muscles, gives you extra strength, and increases mental focus to deal with your emergency. After the emergency is over, your mind signals the adrenal glands to reduce the level of adrenaline in your bloodstream and your body returns back to its pre-emergency state.

Unfortunately, your mind does not know the difference between a real life or death emergency and a major change in your life, an exciting challenge, or a stimulating competition. It's your reaction to this stimulus that alarms your mind to activate your "fight or flight" response. In each case increased adrenaline is produced to help you deal with your situation. The problem is that in our "hurry up" world we are in a near constant state of alarm with elevated levels of adrenaline in our bloodstream.

In short bursts, elevated adrenaline is not damaging or dangerous. That's how God designed your body to work. But a long-term elevated level of adrenaline is devastating to your health. The most serious effect of elevated adrenaline is its damage to the heart and arteries. Other effects of chronic elevated adrenaline include:

- A constriction of the capillaries and other blood vessels that can reduce the blood supply to heart
- An increase in the production of blood cholesterol
- A decrease in the body's ability to remove cholesterol
- An increase in the depositing of plaque on the walls of the arteries
- An increase in the blood's ability to clot.

It's interesting to note that personality type is a good indicator of the likelihood of problems with chronic elevated levels of adrenaline. People with Type-A personalities always have excessive amounts of adrenaline. Do you exhibit the characteristics of a Type-A person? Type-A personality characteristics include:

Always struggling with trying to do more and more in less and less time

- Always in a hurry
- A high degree of competitiveness
- Easily irritated by delays
- A low tolerance for frustration
- Are hard driving and ambitious

- Are highly aggressive
- Cannot relax without feeling guilty
- Are confident on the surface but insecure within
- Have a tendency to finish other people's sentences.

Dr. Archibald Hart says, "A large part of the damage we experience in our lives is caused by "hurry sickness." It comes from our urge to live and do everything in haste. As a consequence, we live at a pace too fast for our bodies. This hurried lifestyle creates a persistent internal state of emergency that keeps our stress hormones elevated."

How can you know if you are under too much stress? The following symptoms and effects may help you determine if you are suffering from too much stress.

Short Term Physical Symptoms

These mainly occur as your body adapts to perceived physical threat, and are caused by release of adrenaline. Although you may perceive these as unpleasant and negative, they are signs that your body is ready for the explosive action that assists survival or high performance:

- Faster heart beat
- Increased sweating
- Cool skin
- Cold hands and feet
- Feelings of nausea, or 'Butterflies in stomach'
- Rapid Breathing
- Tense Muscles
- Dry Mouth
- A desire to urinate
- Diarrhea

These are the symptoms of survival stress.

Short Term Performance Effects

While adrenaline helps you survive in a 'fight-or-flight' situation, it does have negative effects in some situations. Adrenaline can:

- Interfere with clear judgement and makes it difficult to take the time to make good decisions.

- Seriously reduce your enjoyment of your work
- Get in the way of fine motor control.
- Cause difficult situations to be seen as a threat, not a challenge.
- Damage the positive frame of mind you need for high quality work by:
    - promoting negative thinking,
    - damaging self-confidence,
    - narrowing attention,
    - disrupting focus and concentration and
    - making it difficult to cope with distractions
- Consume mental energy in distraction, anxiety, frustration and temper. This is energy that should be devoted to the work in hand.

Long Term Physical Symptoms

These occur when your body has been exposed to adrenaline over a long period. One of the ways adrenaline prepares you for action is by diverting resources to the muscles from the areas of the body which carry out body maintenance. This means that if you are exposed to adrenaline for a sustained period, then your health may start to deteriorate. This may show up in the following ways:

- change in appetite
- frequent colds
- illnesses such as:
    - asthma
    - back pain
    - digestive problems
    - headaches
    - skin eruptions
- sexual disorders
- aches and pains
- feelings of intense and long-term tiredness

Internal Symptoms of Long Term Stress

When you are under stress or have been tired for a long period of time you may find that you are less able to think clearly and rationally about problems. This can lead to the following internal emotional problems:

- Worry or anxiety
- Confusion, and an inability to concentrate or make decisions
- Feeling ill
- Feeling out of control or overwhelmed by events
- Mood changes:
    - Depression
    - Frustration
    - Hostility
    - Helplessness
    - Impatience & irritability
    - Restlessness
- Being more lethargic
- Difficulty sleeping
- Drinking more alcohol and smoking more
- Changing eating habits
- Reduced sex drive
- Relying more on medication

Behavioral Symptoms of Long Term Stress

When you or other people are under pressure, this can show as:

- Talking too fast or too loud
- Yawning
- Fiddling and twitching, nail biting, grinding teeth, drumming fingers, pacing, etc.
- Bad moods:
    - Being irritable
    - Defensiveness
    - Being critical
    - Aggression
    - Irrationality
    - Overreaction and reacting emotionally
- Reduced personal effectiveness:
    - Being unreasonably negative
    - Making less realistic judgements
    - Being unable to concentrate and having difficulty making decisions
    - Being more forgetful
    - Making more mistakes

- Being more accident prone
- Changing work habits
- Increased absenteeism
- Neglect of personal appearance

If you find yourself exhibiting or recognizing a number of these symptoms, it would be worth investigating stress management techniques. The key to managing stress is to get stress to work for you instead of against you. Here are a few tips on how to reduce stress in your life.

1. Identify the causes of stress in your life.
What causes you the most worry and concern? What situations make you feel anxious, nervous or afraid? Once you know what the stressful aspects of your life are, you can learn to deal with them or eliminate them.

2. Share your thoughts and feelings.
It's usually helpful to talk to someone about your concerns. Perhaps a family member, friend, co-worker or member of the clergy can help you see your problems in a different way.

3. Keep an Optimistic Attitude.
Remember that you are responsible for how you feel. Your state of mind is up to you.

4. Simplify your life as much as possible.
Review your daily activities and routine. Prioritize your activities. Simplify or eliminate activities that are not important or of high priority.

5. Manage your time.
Be smart and use your time wisely. There are only 24 hours in a day. Eight hours are reserved for sleep which leaves you 16 hours per day to manage.

6. Keep a "To Do" list.
Keeping a list of daily tasks can remove the pressure of trying to remember them. A "To Do" list actually helps you become more

efficient. You will be able to achieve more each day.

7. Realize that drugs and alcohol don't solve life's problems.
Drugs and alcohol don't solve your problems. They only make them worse.

8. Try to be as physically and mentally healthy as possible.
Exercise is a great stress reliever.

9. Don't be a perfectionist.
Nobody is perfect, we all make mistakes. Always do your best, but don't take it to extremes.

10. Realize that you have the power to change.
If you have a strong desire, you can change any aspect of your life.

11. Practice relaxation techniques.

- Prayer
- Deep breathing
- Meditation
- Yoga
- Listening to quiet, peaceful music

12. Enjoy life.
Don't sweat the small stuff. Laugh and have fun. Don't take life so seriously.

13. Deliberately force yourself to slow down.
Ask yourself "What's the hurry?" Understand that slowing down is not a sign of weakness but a sign of wisdom. Use self-talk to help yourself slow down.

14. Avoid the adrenaline emotions.
Emotions such as anger, frustration, irritation, resentment, and hostility trigger adrenaline production.

15. Seek professional help when needed.
Sometimes the burdens of life are overwhelming and we can't

deal with them by ourselves. Seek help from your pastor, doctor, psychotherapist, or stress management professional.

The mind/body connection is powerful. Your mind can make you feel happy, healthy, and excited about life or it can make you feel depressed, ill, and think that life is not worth living. Make your mind work for you, not against you. Having a personal relationship with God and knowing and obeying His will can put your mind in a state of joy and peace that you've never known before.

> You (God) will show me the way of life, granting me the joy of your presence and the pleasures of living with you forever.
> **Psalms 16:11 (New Living Translation)**

Your mind is the control center for who you are and what you want to become. It's the center for good and evil, joy and sadness, health and sickness. Your thoughts are influenced by many factors, some good and some not so good. Are your thoughts and actions leading you down a path to peace and contentment or are you going down a path leading to sorrow and disaster? I encourage you to spend some time evaluating who you are and where your life is going. Are you satisfied with who you are and where your life is heading? If not, you can change before it's too late. Put your faith and trust in God. Pray right now and tell God you want to change and you need His guidance and strength. God loves you and wants to help you so badly, just ask!

> Finally, brothers, whatever is true, whatever is noble, whatever is right, whatever is pure, whatever is lovely, whatever is admirable—if anything is excellent or praiseworthy—**think** about such things.
>
> Whatever you have learned or received or heard from me, or seen in me—put it into practice. And the God of peace will be with you.
> **Philippians 4:8-9 (New International Version, NIV)**

Spirit

As part of the trinity of humanity, the spirit is the hardest to define. Whereas the body and mind are physical entities, the spirit is invisible and nebulous. Yet, the spirit is even more important than the body and mind in the composition of a wholesome individual. The spirit is a necessary element for good health and an abundant life.

The following chapter will discuss what the spirit is and is not and what the spirit contributes to the trinity of humanity.

CHAPTER 13

The Spirit of Man

When we talk about the spirit of man, what are we really talking about? Are we talking about a state of mind where your outlook is lively and animated, high in spirit? No, it's not about feeling happy and joyful, although this exuberant state of mind can be the result of the spirit. Are we talking about supernatural beings like ghosts? No, we are not talking about ghosts when we refer to the spirit of man. Then, are we talking about the soul? Yes, the spirit and the soul are synonymous terms referring to the spiritual nature of humans, regarded as immortal and separable from the body at death. When we talk about the spirit of man we are really talking about the spirit of God.

When God created you he gave you a body, a mind, and His spirit. God's spirit in you is your direct line of personal communication to your creator. Through God's spirit, also referred to as the Holy Spirit, He comforts you, He guides you, He teaches you right from wrong, He listens to you, He gives you purpose in your life. Unfortunately, many people don't know God's phone number. There is no personal communication between them and God. They miss out on the love, the joy, the happiness, and the purpose of life that only God can provide. No one can be whole without the Holy Spirit controlling their life.

I can tell you from personal testimony that there was a time in my life when I had no communication with God. I didn't know God's phone number. I was in control of my life instead of God. By American standards I had a good life. I had a good job, a wonderful family, a house, and 2 cars. Yet, I felt lonely, unloved, and depressed. I had no purpose for my life, no reason to get excited about life. Something was missing in my life. Then I had a life changing experience! I found God's phone number.

I no longer control my life. I let God control my life. He does a much better job than I ever did. Now I experience the joy and peace and love that only God can provide. I have purpose for my life and reason to get excited about life. Each day is a new exciting adventure.

Would you like to know God's phone number so you can personally communicate with Him? God's phone number is JESUS CHRIST.

> For there is one God and one mediator between God and men, the man Christ Jesus.
> **1 Timothy 2:5 (New International Version, NIV)**

In the beginning, God created Adam and Eve and placed them in the Garden of Eden to live happily ever after in the presence of God. But, Adam and Eve sinned. God was so angry with Adam and Eve that He kicked them out of the Garden of Eden and doomed them and all their descendents to a life of hard labor and ultimate death. Ultimate death being eternal separation from God. The line of communication between God and man was severed.

Because of Adam and Eve's sinful act, everyone born into this world is born with a sinful nature. We live in a world where evilness, wrongdoing, death, and separation from God are the norm. This is very evident when observing our society today. The sinful nature of man is also evident in children. You never have to teach children to be disobedient, it comes naturally.

Even though the spirit of God is in you since your creation, it is weak or dormant due to your separation from God. Your sinful nature controls your life resulting in your disobedience, condemnation, and ultimate death. Your disobedience to God's way of living is why you don't have the vibrant health and abundant life you desire.

We are very fortunate to have a God that loves us. Through His grace He gave man a second chance to reestablish the line of communication with Him and enjoy His love and holiness and experience eternal life with Him in heaven. God gave us His son, Jesus Christ, as a means of reestablishing communication with Him.

> For God so loved the world that he gave his one and

> only Son, that whoever believes in him shall not perish but have eternal life.
> **John 3:16 (New International Version, NIV)**

Putting your faith and trust in Jesus establishes your personal line of communication with God. You can now enjoy the love and happiness and purpose that your heavenly Father wants you to experience. And you are assured eternal life with Him in heaven. Putting your faith and trust in Jesus awakens the Holy Spirit within you. Allowing the Holy Spirit to control your life will allow you to enjoy vibrant health and abundant life.

> I (Jesus) have come that they may have life, and that they may have it more abundantly.
> **John 10:10 (New King James Version)**

Would you like to reestablish your line of communication to God through Jesus? Here's what you have to do:

1. Understand that you are a sinner and that your sin leads to eternal death – eternal separation from God.

   > For all have sinned and fall short of the glory of God.
   > **Romans 3:23 (New International Version, NIV)**

   > For the wages of sin is death.
   > **Romans 6:23 (New International Version, NIV)**

2. Be willing to change and turn from your sins (repent).

   > But unless you repent, you too will all perish.
   > **Luke 13:3 (New International Version, NIV)**

3. Turn to Jesus Christ. You must believe with your whole heart that Jesus paid the ultimate price for your sin by dying on the cross. You must believe that Jesus arose from the grave after three days fulfilling the scripture and demonstrating that there is everlasting life in Jesus.

   > Christ died for our sins according to the Scriptures, that he was buried, that he was raised on the third

> day according to the Scriptures.
> **1 Corinthians 15:3-4 (New International Version, NIV)**

> That if you confess with your mouth, "Jesus is Lord," and believe in your heart that God raised him from the dead, you will be saved.
> **Romans 10:9 (New International Version, NIV)**

4. Through prayer, invite Jesus Christ to come in and control your life through the Holy Spirit. Recite the following prayer:

    Dear Lord Jesus,
    I know that I am a sinner and need Your forgiveness. I believe that You died for my sins. I want to turn from my sins. I now invite You to come into my heart and life. I want to trust, follow and obey You as my Lord and Savior.
    In Jesus' name I pray, Amen.

   If you prayed this prayer, congratulations! Welcome to the family of Christ. Welcome to the new eternal life that only Jesus can bring.

> "Everyone who calls on the name of the Lord will be saved."
> **Romans 10:13 (New International Version, NIV)**

This is just the beginning of your wonderful new life in Christ. To develop and grow this relationship you should:

1. Read your Bible everyday to learn and understand the word of God.
2. Talk to God in prayer every day.
3. Take what you learn from God and put it into action. He has a plan for your life!
4. Worship, fellowship, and serve with other Christians in a

church where God's word is preached and obeyed.
5. Tell others about Christ.

Maybe you're a long time Christian. You've gone to church your whole life and you established your communication with God at an early age. Yet, you are not experiencing the joy, vibrant health, and abundant life that God promised. Maybe your communication with God has gotten a little fuzzy. Perhaps you have gotten a bit lazy or rebellious and have not been talking, listening, or obeying God as you know you should. Don't give up, there is still hope for you. It's never too late to get a fresh start and rejuvenate your relationship with God. Maybe you have one of the older analog lines of communication to God. You know the type of communication line that has a lot of static and dropouts. You need to upgrade to the new digital quality communication with God. Digital communication with God is crystal clear.

Joking aside, many Christians know God in their head, but not in their heart. God knows the difference. You study the Bible and know all about God. Yet, you've never surrendered your life to Him. You've never allowed the Holy Spirit to take control and do wonderful things with your life. You see, not only do we need to know God mentally, we need to know Him spiritually.

In the book of Revelation there is a letter to the church in Laodicea. God is concerned that the members of this church are serving more than one master. They call themselves God's people, yet their pride, arrogance, and self-reliance allows them to worship the secular world. God is angered that they have one foot in God's world and the other foot in the secular world, trying to get the best from both worlds. God vows to cast them away unless they repent.

> I know your deeds, that you are neither cold nor hot. I wish you were either one or the other! So, because you are lukewarm—neither hot nor cold—I am about to spit you out of my mouth.
> **Revelation 3:15-16 (New International Version, NIV)**

Are you serving two masters? Are you pretending to be one of God's people while serving the secular world? Although it's true that we all must live *in* the world, we don't have to live *of* the world. In other words, just because we live in the secular world doesn't mean we have to conform to the standards of the secular world. Conform to God's standards and let the Holy Spirit lead you to happiness, health, and abundant life.

> 'What's the use of serving God? What have we gained by obeying his commands or by trying to show the LORD Almighty that we are sorry for our sins?
>
> "They will be my people," says the LORD Almighty. "On the day when I act, they will be my own special treasure. I will spare them as a father spares an obedient and dutiful child.
> **Malachi 3:14, 17 (New Living Translation)**

In the book of Revelation there is also a letter to the church in Sardis. God is concerned that the church of Sardis is dying. Once the people were alive and following God's way. Now they are dead. The people lost their zeal and passion for God and are not doing what is right in God's eyes. God warns them to go back and renew their faith and passion or they will suffer the consequences.

> I know your deeds; you have a reputation of being alive, but you are dead. Wake up! Strengthen what remains and is about to die, for I have not found your deeds complete in the sight of my God. Remember, therefore, what you have received and heard; obey it, and repent. But if you do not wake up, I will come like a thief, and you will not know at what time I will come to you.
> **Revelation 3:1-3 (New International Version, NIV)**
>
> For we must all appear before the judgment seat of Christ, that each one may receive what is due him for the things done while in the body, whether good or bad.
> **2 Corinthians 5:10 (New International Version, NIV)**

Have you lost your zeal and passion for God? I encourage you to ask God to revitalize your personal relationship with Him. Your passion and love for God can be restored if you sincerely make the effort. The return of a lost lamb always warms the heart of the good shepherd.

> If a man owns a hundred sheep, and one of them wanders away, will he not leave the ninety-nine on the hills and go to look for the one that wandered off? And if he finds it, I tell you the truth, he is happier about that one sheep than about the ninety-nine that did not wander off.
> **Matthew 18:12-13 (New International Version, NIV)**

I don't know the state of your personal relationship with God. But, I do know a life without God is not whole. The Holy Spirit of God is an essential element of the trinity of humanity. It works together with the body and mind to produce a wholesome individual in harmony with God. The Holy Spirit is your personal communication link to God. The Holy Spirit brings you God's love, guidance, and understanding of right and wrong. The Holy Spirit will lead you away from your sinful nature to an obedient life with God. A life of joy, peace, and abundance!

> When you follow the desires of your sinful nature, your lives will produce these evil results: sexual immorality, impure thoughts, eagerness for lustful pleasure, idolatry, participation in demonic activities, hostility, quarreling, jealousy, outbursts of anger, selfish ambition, divisions, the feeling that everyone is wrong except those in your own little group, envy, drunkenness, wild parties, and other kinds of sin. Let me tell you again, as I have before, that anyone living that sort of life will not inherit the Kingdom of God. But when the Holy Spirit controls our lives, he will produce this kind of fruit in us: love, joy, peace, patience, kindness, goodness, faithfulness, gentleness, and self-control. Here there is no conflict with the law.

Those who belong to Christ Jesus have nailed the passions and desires of their sinful nature to his cross and crucified them there. If we are living now by the Holy Spirit, let us follow the Holy Spirit's leading in every part of our lives.
Galatians 5:19-25 (New Living Translation)

Section III - A Healthy Plan for Abundant Life

Putting it all together – Development, refinement, and rejuvenation of the Body, Mind and Spirit achieving your full potential for the glory of God

CHAPTER 14

Analysis

By the time you reach this part of the book, I pray that you are anxious to make some changes in your life that will impact your health for the glory of God. You may have already identified some specific area of the body, mind, or spirit that needs some work but you're not sure how to get started. The purpose of this section is to guide you through a systematic process to help get you where you want to go on the road to better health. The first step is to analyze your current state of health.

Before you start on your journey to better health, you need to know your starting place. If you are planning on driving to New York and want to map your driving route, you need to know your starting point. Is your starting point Dallas or Miami? Your journey will be significantly different depending on your starting point. It's the same with your journey to better health. You must analyze your current situation to understand where you are now on the road to health. Some of you are on the straight and narrow road, some of you have taken detours, some of you have fallen by the way side and some of you are wandering around lost and don't have a clue as to where you are. It doesn't matter where you are now, you just need to find your starting point so you can create a plan to get you where God wants you to be.

Your first step is to analyze your current health situation through various assessments for the body, mind, and spirit. I've provided a health assessment worksheet in Appendix D for your use. Fill out the worksheet as completely as possible and save it. I recommend that you use this worksheet to make evaluation and recommendation notes. These notes will help you later when setting goals. You should do a reassessment every six to twelve months and compare the results with previous assessments to check your progress.

Let's start with assessing the current state of your physical body.

In general, I always recommend that you go to your physician for a physical exam. Tell your doctor that you want to start an exercise program and ask him if you need to impose any exercise limitations due to your current physical condition. Children should also consult with their physician about exercise limitations if they have any health problems or are taking medication. The physical parameters that you want to record on your worksheet are body weight, blood pressure, blood cholesterol levels, resting heart rate, current health problems, and current medications.

I want to caution you. Visiting your physician for a physical exam is vitally important. It could save you a lot of discomfort, pain, and even save your life! Many of you have not kept up with a regular exercise program and may not have had a physical in years. You may be totally unaware of possible health conditions that you may have such as heart disease or diabetes. Heart disease is the number one cause of death in this country. Participating in intense exercise programs with such a medical condition could be life threatening. This is a situation where it is better to error on the side of caution. Of course, if you just had a physical exam over the last few months or are currently under the regular care of a physician, it's possible that a phone call to your physician inquiring about exercise limitations due to your health condition or medications will suffice.

Next, you will want to do a fitness assessment. Go to a health club or fitness center and have a trainer put you through a battery of tests. You want to assess all five of the fitness components:

1. Aerobic Endurance
2. Muscular Strength
3. Muscular Endurance
4. Flexibility
5. Body Composition

If you are currently not a member of a health club you may find it difficult to complete your fitness assessment. Try calling a few health clubs and ask if they will do a fitness assessment for you without being a member. Many clubs offer free fitness assessments to new members.

You may be thinking, I haven't exercised in many years and I know that I'm really out of shape. Going through a fitness assessment would be insulting and a waste of time. If you're in this situation, I agree. You can pass on the formal fitness assessment. You can do a few basic fitness assessments at home or in a neighborhood park. For instance, timing yourself in a one-mile walk will serve as an aerobic endurance assessment. Doing pushups and situps will serve as a muscular endurance assessment. Flexibility can be assessed by bending over and touching your toes from a standing position and noting how far you can stretch. Girth measurements will serve as your body composition assessment. Use a measuring tape and measure the circumference of several body parts. Use your assessment worksheet as a guide for girth measurements.

Be sure to record the results of each assessment on your worksheet. Even if you complete zero pushups or situps, mark it down. That's your starting point. You'll be amazed at the progress you will make in six months when you do a reassessment.

That completes the body assessment. Now, let's assess the current state of your mind. You want to evaluate your character and your attitude. Appendix C is a Character Assessment. If you have already completed the Character Assessment just transfer your score to your assessment worksheet. Otherwise, complete the Character Assessment now and write your score on the assessment worksheet.

Attitude characteristics describe your general outlook on life. Table 14-1 contains a list of attitude characteristics. For each pair (one in the left hand column and one in the right hand column) of attitude characteristics circle the characteristic that best describes you most of the time. Be honest. Better yet, have a family member or close friend do this assessment on your behalf. It's often eye opening to know how others view you.

Attitude Check	
Cheerful	Gloomy
Expect the Best	Expect the Worst
Upbeat	Depressed
Challenged	Frustrated
Loving	Cold
Generous	Selfish
Obedient	Nonconforming
Reasonable	Unreasonable
Energetic	Lethargic
Humble	Prideful
Easygoing	Worried
Excited	Apathetic
Determined	Hesitant
Confident	Fearful
Encouraging	Complaining
Courteous	Overbearing

Table 14-1

Once you have completed the attitude check, count the number of circled words in the left-hand column. If you scored 1-7, you have a mostly negative attitude about life. If you scored 8-9, you have a neutral attitude (an equal number of both positive and negative characteristics). If scored 10-16, you have a mostly positive attitude. Mark your score on the assessment worksheet.

Finally, let's do a spiritual assessment. Answer the following questions to assess your current relationship with God. Read each sentence and score it according to the criteria in the rating scale below.

Spiritual Assessment						
Question	**Rating Scale**					**Score**
	Very Seldom	Sometimes	Usually	Most of the Time	Almost Always	
1. I am obedient to God's will.	1	2	3	4	5	
2. I let the Holy Spirit control my life.	1	2	3	4	5	
3. I study God's word daily.	1	2	3	4	5	
4. I pray to God daily.	1	2	3	4	5	
5. I exhibit Godly characteristics in my everyday life	1	2	3	4	5	
6. I tell others about Jesus.	1	2	3	4	5	
					Total Score	

Scoring

25 - 30	You have a great relationship with God.
18 – 24	There is room for improvement.
5 - 17	You need to work very hard at building your relationship with God.

Table 14-2

After you complete the Spiritual Assessment, mark your score on the assessment worksheet.

You have completed the analysis step and should have a good idea of your strengths and weaknesses. You now have a starting point for preparing goals and a plan to help you reach your full potential for the glory of God. As you analyzed the various assessments that you completed, you may have noticed several areas that need improvement. Don't be discouraged, you are just finding your starting point on the road to good health. Remember that God is with you. He wants you to be victorious in your quest for health and abundant life. Just ask Him for the strength and perseverance to reach victory.

> The LORD is my strength and my song; he has become my victory.
> **Psalms 118:14 (New Living Translation)**

CHAPTER 15

Goals

Now that you found your starting point on the road to better health you need to decide where you want to go. You do this by setting goals. What is a goal? A goal is a desired outcome toward which effort is directed. When you set a goal you are working to achieve a specific end result.

Why set goals? Setting goals allows you to choose where you want to go in life. By knowing what you want to achieve, you know where your efforts need to be focused. By setting clearly defined goals, you can measure the achievement of your goals. You will see forward progress in your life instead of leading a life that is standing still or wandering about aimlessly. Goals help define your purpose in life. Very often, if you don't set goals for yourself, someone will set goals for you. People that don't set goals always end up disappointed with their life.

By setting goals you can:

- Achieve more
- Improve performance
- Increase your motivation to achieve
- Improve your self-confidence
- Suffer less from stress and anxiety

Is goal setting scriptural? Does God desire us to set goals? The Bible is full of examples of goal setting. Not only does God want us to set goals; He often sets goals for us. God set a goal for Noah to build an ark. What would have happened if Noah didn't have this goal of building an ark? All living creatures on earth, including man, would have been destroyed. God set a goal for Moses to lead the Israelites to the Promised Land. God set a goal for John the Baptist to prepare the way for the Messiah. God even set the goal for Jesus to die on the cross for our sins so that you and I might have salvation and eternal life. Thank God for goal setting!

God definitely wants us to set goals. If you listen to Him He will even help you set your goals. Many people never set goals in their life and never really seem to get anywhere in life nor do they have the abundant life that Jesus would like you to have. Perhaps you don't know how to set goals or you feel that goal setting is a waste of time. Maybe you've tried setting goals and you just never accomplished them, so you gave up. Leave all those ill feelings about goal setting behind you. We are going to start fresh and learn how to set clear, measurable, and realistic goals God's way.

First of all, before formulating any goals you need to understand your purpose in life. Why is knowing your purpose in life important? Your purpose is the underlying reason behind your goal setting. You are setting goals to fulfill your purpose or mission in life. Purpose gives you a reason to set goals.

What is the difference between having and not having a purpose? Without purpose you are like a ship without an engine or rudder, out of control, unable to choose your direction. You don't know where you are going. You are at the mercy of the wind and currents to control your direction. You feel insecure and confused about what may happen to you. Without purpose, fear and doubt permeate your thoughts. You settle for living in a rut and are usually disappointed with your life.

With purpose you are like a ship with a destination, heading in a set direction. You are in control. You know exactly where you are going. With purpose, confidence and trust dominate your demeanor. You are a person who strives for excellence and is excited about life.

As we discuss purpose in your life, I want you to know that I'm referring to God's purpose in your life. You see Satan also has a purpose for your life, but you don't want to follow his purpose. It will only lead you astray. Saul of Tarsus had a purpose in life. His mission was to persecute Christians. God eventually straightened him out and changed his purpose in life to a Godly purpose of teaching and promoting Christianity. You need to be cautious about the source of your life purpose. Only God can provide you with a purpose worth achieving.

If you don't already know your Godly purpose in life you need to get in touch with God to get an understanding of His purpose for your life. We all have multiple purposes in life. The Bible tells us about God's purpose for all of us. The Bible explicitly tells us that God has given all of us the purpose of worshiping and serving HIM. God has given us the purpose of being good stewards of all that He has created on this earth. God has even given us the purpose of telling others about the Good News. The news of Jesus Christ!

> Give to the Lord the glory due His name; Bring an offering, and come before Him. Oh, worship the Lord in the beauty of holiness!
> **1 Chronicles 16:29 (New King James Version)**

> "And now, Israel, what does the Lord your God require of you, but to fear the Lord your God, to walk in all His ways and to love Him, to serve the Lord your God with all your heart and with all your soul."
> **Deuteronomy 10:12 (New King James Version)**

> . . . "They (Human Beings) will be masters over all life – the fish in the sea, the birds in the sky, and all the livestock, wild animals, and small animals."
> **Genesis 1:26 (New Living Translation)**

> "Go therefore and make disciples of all the nations, baptizing them in the name of the Father and of the Son and of the Holy Spirit, teaching them to observe all things that I have commanded you; and lo, I am with you always, even to the end of the age."
> **Matthew 28:19-20 (New King James Version)**

In addition, God put us on this earth for a specific purpose. God has given us a specific purpose of vocation, maybe a school teacher, or a doctor, or a minister. God may have given you a purpose of being a spouse and a parent. Maybe you've never asked God His desires for your life. I never dreamed that I would be writing a Godly book on health, but this is what God wanted me to do, so I did it. I set a goal to write this book and achieved it with His help. God has something special in mind for you as well. Ask Him for help in clarifying your purpose in life and ask for His guidance in setting goals.

> I will instruct you and teach you in the way you should go; I will counsel you and watch over you.
> **Psalms 32:8 (New International Version, NIV)**

As you discover your Godly purpose in life, here are some questions to ponder and ask God:

- Why am I here?
- What is my reason for being?
- Who am I?
- Do I like who I am?
- Why am I not satisfied and fulfilled?
- What are my strong desires and passions?
- God, how can I serve you?

Once you become familiar with your life purpose you have some direction on which to base your goals. You want to create SMART Goals. These are goals that are Specific, Measurable, Action Oriented, Realistic, and Time Specific.

SMART Goals

Specific: Provide enough detail to understand exactly what you should be doing. Goals that are too general don't provide enough direction and often don't get accomplished. For example a goal of "I want to get healthy" is too general. You don't know where to begin towards accomplishing this goal. There must be at least 20 to 30 things you can think of that will help you improve your health. This general statement "I want to get healthy" is not a specific goal, it is really more of a desire and it may serve as a good starting point for developing goals. Strong desires and passions can often be good starting points for developing goals.

You have established the fact that you want to improve your health. Now develop specific goals that will get you closer towards achieving good health. A specific goal might be "I will jog around the park 3 days per week." This goal defines what to do (jog), where to do it (park) and how often to do it (3 days per week).

Measurable: Your goal needs to have some means of determining achievement. If your goal is "I want to be healthy," how will you ever know if you achieved it? There are no concrete criteria on which to base your achievement. On the other hand, your goal that states "I will jog around the park 3 days per week" has criteria for achievement and it's very clear to know whether or not you achieved this goal.

Action Oriented: Your goal needs to have some action as a means of accomplishment. If you don't take action, your goal will never become reality! There is no action for the goal "I want to be healthy." Your goal "I will jog around the park 3 days per week" has jogging as the action. This goal can be accomplished.

Realistic: Evaluate your goal to determine if it is reasonable and it can be achieved. If you evaluate the goal "I want to lose 100 pounds in 2 months" you'll see that this goal is both unreasonable and cannot be achieved. Healthy weight loss is about 2 pounds per week. This means you should only expect to lose about 16 pounds in 2 months. If you modify your goal to read "I want to lose 100 pounds in 12 months" you now have a goal that is reasonable and achievable. Losing 2 pounds per week for 52 weeks would mean a weight loss of 104 pounds. Sometimes you may not know if your goals are reasonable or achievable. That's when it's time to do some research or get the advice of a competent expert.

Ask yourself "Does achieving this goal get me closer to fulfilling my purpose?" If your answer is no, then don't waste your time achieving this goal. Either forget about this goal or modify it so that it does move you closer to fulfilling your purpose.

Also, ask yourself "Will I do what is necessary to achieve this goal?" If your answer is no, don't even get started because you've already set yourself up for failure. Sometimes people set great goals on paper but don't have the desire or passion to carry them through to completion. Set goals that you believe you *can* and *will* achieve.

Time Specific: Make sure that your goals set a specific date or time for completion. Otherwise, they could go on forever. Goals without time specification often get pushed to the side for higher priority activities. Goals that are time specific help you plan your daily activities and have a much greater chance of being accomplished.

ALWAYS write down your goals. Your goals will contain a significant amount of detail that you will forget over time. Keep your written goals in a place where you can review them often. Monitor your progress towards your goals and modify them if necessary. When you create your goals evaluate each goal against the SMART criteria and modify them as needed.

Write down your goal – I will join the XYZ health club by January 1, 2003. Then ask yourself:

1. Is this goal **specific**? YES, I know exactly what I need to do.
2. Is this goal **measurable**? YES, I can easily determine whether I accomplish this goal or not.
3. Is this goal **action oriented**? YES, I need to take action to join the health club.
4. Is this goal **realistic**? YES, it is reasonable and achievable. Achieving this goal will get me a step closer to improving my health. I can and will achieve this goal.
5. Is this goal **time specific**? YES, it must be completed by January 1, 2003.

If your goal meets all these criteria, congratulations, you have a SMART goal that will provide you direction and move you closer to achieving your purpose.

I recommend that you double-check each goal by asking one more question. Can I honestly ask God for help in achieving this goal? Sometimes people can get carried away and set some goals that are very self-serving. These self-serving goals often put undue hardships on family and friends or may violate other people's rights. If your goal does not violate your conscience and you can honestly ask God for help in achieving your goal then you can feel all the more certain that you have a goal worth achieving.

Goals fall into three categories, immediate, short-term, and long-term. Immediate goals are goals that are to be completed within one week. Short-term goals are goals that are to be completed between one week and up to one year. Long-term goals are goals that take one-year or more to complete. It is advisable to create goals for all three categories. Very often it takes one or more immediate goals to achieve a short-term goal and one or more short-term goals to achieve a long-term goal.

Let me show you how long-term, short-term and immediate goals can work together for you. Let's say that I set a long-term goal of losing 100 pounds in one year. A year is a long time. How will I be able to monitor my progress and know if I'm on track to achieve this goal? You can't, the time span of this goal is too long to know if you're staying on track. If I get off track during the early part of the year I won't know it and there's no telling where I will end up by the end of the year. You can solve this problem by breaking the one-year time frame into smaller time frames. You can create a short-term goal. I can create a short-term goal of losing 8.5 pounds per month for 12 months. Now I know that if I lose 8.5 pounds per month for the next 12 months I will reach my long-term goal of losing 100 pounds in one year. The short-term goal makes it much easier to monitor my progress and know if I'm on track. I can reduce the time frame of my short-term goal even further by creating an immediate goal. I can create an immediate goal of losing 2 pounds per week for the next 52 weeks. I know that if I lose 2 pounds for the next 52 weeks I will reach my goal of losing 100 pounds in one year. I can monitor my progress weekly and quickly make adjustments should I get off track.

Make sure that your goals are easy to monitor within a reasonable period of time. Knowing that you are on track to reach your goal is a confidence builder. Knowing that you slipped and are off track is also important because it allows you to quickly make adjustments and get back on track to ultimately reach your goal.

In this book we have dealt with goals that are health oriented. Goal setting applies to every aspect of your life. Besides setting goals for your health (body, mind, and spirit), you should also set goals dealing with family, finances, career, and social life.

Now that you know how to set goals, it's time to practice. Write down at least 10 goals for improving or maintaining your health. Remember that health pertains to the body, mind and spirit. Create immediate, short-term, and long-term goals. Go back to your Assessment Worksheet from the previous chapter and use it as a guide for determining areas of improvement and potential goals. You will use these goals in the next chapter.

It is God's desire for you to be happy, healthy, and prosperous. Will you let Him help you reach that goal? Write down your goals and ask God for the help and guidance to achieve them. Seek His will, trust in Him and He will help you.

> Commit your way to the Lord, Trust also in Him, And He shall bring it to pass.
> **Psalms 37:7 (New King James Version)**

CHAPTER 16

The Plan

You found your starting point on the road to better health (analysis), you decided where you want to go (set goals), now you need to map your route on how to get there. Planning is simply an organized method for achieving your end result. Your plan is a detailed formulation of a program of action.

From the previous chapter on goal setting you have prepared a list of at least 10 goals. Now you will take those goals and prepare a plan for achieving each goal. Take a piece of paper and start by writing down your purpose followed by your goal to achieve your purpose. Then write down the actions you need to take in order to achieve your goal. See Table 16-1 for an example.

Your Plan to Achievement

Purpose: Good stewardship – improve my health

Long-Term Goal: Lose 100 pounds in 12 months, beginning 1/1/03 and ending 12/31/03

Short-Term Goal: Lose 8.5 pounds per month between 1/1/03 and 12/31/03

Immediate Goal: Lose 2 pounds per week between 1/1/03 and 12/31/03

Plan for Achieving This Goal:

Body

- Drink at least 8 eight ounce glasses of pure water per day
- Eat a low fat diet
- Eliminate junk foods from my diet (cookies, candy, cakes, ice cream, chips)
- Eat more raw fruits and vegetables

- Supplement with a multiple vitamin/mineral formula
- Cardiovascular exercise (walking) 6 days per week (gradually increasing distance, time and speed)
- Strength Exercise (weights) 3 days per week (gradually increasing weight and sets)
- Practice deep breathing exercise

Mind

- Associate with people that are encouraging and supportive
- Reduce television time
- Increase reading of material that will enhance my mind
- Participate in activities or hobbies that will keep my mind off of food

Spirit

- Pray to God for strength, courage and perseverance to achieve this goal
- Read my Bible for better understanding of God's word (research passages that deal with health, abundant life, gluttony, and worshipping false idols)
- Share with others my testimony on how God has guided and encouraged me to change my ways and become a good steward of my health

NOTE: This plan for weight loss is an example and is not intended to be used as a complete program for weight loss.

Table 16-1

It is usually best to further define long-term goals into some short-term goals. Doing this allows you to plan your actions over shorter time periods, which helps you monitor your progress towards your long-term goal, and gives you more opportunity to celebrate your achievements by accomplishing several short-term goals enroute to your long-term success. If practical, for the same reasons, short-term goals may be further defined into immediate goals.

I want to take a minute to talk about weight loss. American's are obsessed with weight loss. American's spend millions of dollars on fad diets and weight loss programs each year, yet American's are getting more and more overweight.. Most people that lose weight on these fad diets and various weight loss programs gain it all back within a year. Focusing your efforts on weight loss does not get you healthy. It may reduce your risk of disease, but even thin people die of heart attack, cancer, and stroke. Focus your efforts on building your health, not on weight loss. It's fine to have a goal of losing weight, but it should be one part of a health building program. Weight control is a byproduct of a maintaining good health.

Now you've got the basic idea on how to create a plan for achieving your goals. Whenever you create a goal, write down the actions necessary to achieve your goal. Keep in mind that sometimes you may not know how to achieve your goal. That's okay. You'll need to do some research and/or talk with knowledgeable people who can advise you.

Health Promoting Actions

This section is designed to help you plan your actions for improving your health. Following is a listing of different health improving tips that you may choose from when preparing your plans to reach your health goals. Remember that good health requires the body, mind, and spirit to work together. Keep these three entities in balance.

Body

Use all natural soap, shampoo, detergent, and toothpaste.

Nutrition

1. Drink at least 8 eight ounce glasses of pure water every day.
2. Eat more raw fruits and vegetables – make juice if desired.
3. Take a quality multiple vitamin/mineral supplement.
4. Insure regular bowel elimination – 1-3 times daily
5. Detoxify your colon – quarterly colon cleansing.
6. Consume Essential Fatty Acids – Fish oil, flax seed.
7. Reduce refined sugar consumption.
8. Reduce hydrogenated fat consumption.
9. Eliminate tobacco products.
10. Eliminate drinking alcohol.
11. Reduce processed foods.
12. Eliminate coffee.
13. Eat breakfast – it's the most important meal of the day.
14. Keep your body acid/alkalinity balanced.

15. Get plenty of sunshine but don't burn.
16. Eat only meats that God designed for your food – no pork.
17. If feeling hungry – drink water and/or snack on fruit or vegetables.
18. Use organic products whenever possible.
19. Eliminate the use of artificial sweeteners - Aspartame.
20. Don't take prescription or over the counter drugs unless absolutely necessary.

Exercise

1. Stay active – participate in sports, gardening, housework, hiking, camping, etc.
2. Begin an aerobic exercise program 3-6 times per week.
3. Begin a strength training program 2-3 times per week.
4. Walk instead of taking the car.
5. Take the stairs instead of the elevator.
6. Perform deep breathing exercises twice a day.

Sleep / Relaxation

1. Get 7-8 hours of sleep for adults every night.
2. Keep a regular bed time schedule – go to bed at the same time nightly.
3. Take a break from your regular routine, the body needs to recuperate from a hectic week. Allow one day out of seven for rest.

Mind

1. Slow down, love, be happy, relax, and enjoy life.
2. Focus on the positive, not the negative.
3. Focus your thoughts on others, not yourself.
4. Reduce time watching television – too negative.
5. Educate yourself – read, take classes.
6. Always expect the best – strive for excellence.
7. Keep your mind active – use it or lose it!
8. Meditate on God's word.
9. Use self-talk to counter negative thinking.

Spirit

1. Read your Bible
2. Submit to God
3. Listen to God
4. Worship God
5. Pray to God
6. Witness for God
7. Work for God

General Guidelines and Bits of Information

Most Americans choose their foods based on appearance, taste, and aroma with little or no concern about nutritive value. Consequently, the foods that most Americans choose to eat provide more toxins and anti-nutrients than nourishment. In order to change your eating habits from tearing down your health to building up your health you need to change your perspective on how you select foods. Make nourishment your number one selection criteria for choosing your foods with appearance, taste, and aroma being secondary.

Because of the unhealthy lifestyles that American's lead, constipation is a major problem in our society today. Since disease often begins in the colon, it's important to make sure the colon is eliminating toxins on a regular basis. If you are not experiencing 1-3 easy bowel movements per day, you need to take action. Increasing your water and fiber intake will often alleviate constipation problems. A vitamin C flush or herbs cascara sagrada and senna leaves are also recommended for cleaning out the colon.

Keep your life in balance. Your body, mind and spirit work together in harmony with God. Strive for a balance that promotes good health. Take responsibility for your health and change your ways as needed to glorify God. Remember the circle diagrams that you were introduced to back in Chapter 1? See Figure 16-1. For optimal health the three entities of the trinity of humanity must reach a point of excellence where they overlap and strengthen one another.

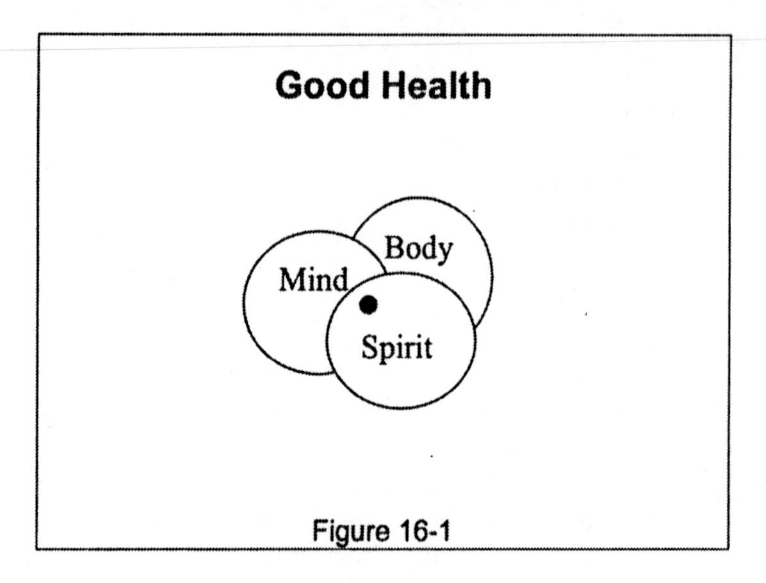

Figure 16-1

Find a role model that emulates the good health diagram above. Find a person that is sound in body, mind, and spirit; a person of impeccable character, a leader that takes action in all aspects of his or her life for the glory of God. Find out what makes that person tick and learn from them. Apply what you learn to your own life. Your role model might be someone in your family or someone in your local community or even someone you admire from afar.

One of my favorite role models is Cal Ripken Jr., a baseball player from the Baltimore Orioles. Cal is a humble man who strives for excellence and always gives his very best. Cal has an incredible work ethic. His job was to play baseball and that's exactly what he did. And he did it better than anyone else. In fact he never missed a game in 15 years. He set a major league record of playing 2,632 consecutive games, more than anybody in the history of baseball. What an incredible accomplishment. Can you imagine what you could accomplish for the glory of God if you applied Cal Ripken's work ethic to your life!

Reduce your stress. Even good stress that continues for a prolonged time can weaken your immune system and expose you to illness and disease. Too much stress can cause many symptoms such as fatigue, pain and stiffness of muscles and joints, dizziness, nausea and vomiting, anxiety, gastrointestinal problems (poor digestion, diarrhea, and constipation) and headaches to name a few.

Excessive stress is also associated with major disease such as heart disease, cancer, and stroke. Slow down your hectic pace of life. Don't push yourself to the point of exhaustion and illness. God designed your body with a healthy stress limitation. Heed your human stress limitations and reduce your activities, learn to say "No," and get plenty of sleep.

Due to your hectic lifestyle you may find it difficult to fall asleep at bedtime or stay asleep all night. If you experience sleep problems try drinking herbal teas or taking natural formulas designed for sleep and relaxation about one hour before bedtime. These bedtime herbal formulas usually contain herbs such as passionflower, valerian root, catnip, and chamomile. Also, try performing deep breathing exercises to ease tension. Melatonin, a natural hormone that promotes sleep can also help, but don't over do it, follow instructions. Prescription sleeping pills are never the answer to help promote healthy, restful sleep.

If you are starting an exercise program and don't know how to begin, seek the services of a personal trainer. In just a few sessions you can have a sound exercise program designed just for you. When beginning an exercise program start easy and gradually increase the intensity of exercise over time to keep your program challenging. Any strenuous exercise session should begin with a warm up period. I'm referring to exercise sessions such as moderate to heavy strength training, intense aerobic exercise like running sprints, or competitive sports. Take about five minutes to warm up and prepare the body for strenuous exercise. Jogging, calisthenics, weight training exercises with light weights and 10-15 repetitions, and stretching all qualify as good ways to warm up. Preparing your body for intense exercise will make your exercise sessions more productive and greatly reduce your risk for injury.

Take Action

The most important part of any plan is putting it into action. Many people take the time to set goals and make plans but never put them into action. Plans never put into action will never bear fruit. In order to achieve God's goals for your life *you* must take action.

I find three main reasons for people failing to take action. They are misplaced priorities or desires, apathy or indifference, and slothfulness. God teaches us that His desires come first. Too often we put our selfish desires ahead of God's desires and just never get around to taking action on what pleases God. God tells us that He desires happiness, health, and prosperity for all of us. Put God's desires first and take action, you shall succeed.

> The old sinful nature loves to do evil, which is just opposite from what the Holy Spirit wants. And the Spirit gives us desires that are opposite from what the sinful nature desires. These two forces are constantly fighting each other, and your choices are never free from this conflict.
> **Galatians 5:17 (New Living Translation)**

The second reason for people not taking action is apathy or indifference. Sometimes people who aren't following God's way experience frustration, rejection, and failure to a point where they just give up and don't care anymore. This is indifference. An example of this is a person who wants to lose weight and bounces from fad diet to fad diet and quick weight loss program to quick weight loss program with no favorable results and maybe even losing ground by gaining more weight. After a while this person gives up, doesn't care anymore, and tries to accept that they'll always be overweight. Rather than becoming indifferent, turn to God for a plan of action.

> I am the one who corrects and disciplines everyone I love. Be diligent and turn from your indifference.
> **Revelation 3:19 (New Living Translation)**

The final reason for people not taking action is slothfulness. Some people are just plain lazy. Despite knowing better they just won't take any action. God warns us that laziness is a very destructive behavior leading to our own destruction. There is no excuse for laziness. Understand that it's God's desire for you to take action and work for His glory. You have two choices, work hard and become a leader for God or be lazy and become a slave of the evil one. Which do you choose?

> The desires of lazy people will be their ruin, for their

hands refuse to work.
Proverbs 21:25 (New Living Translation)

A lazy person is as bad as someone who destroys things.
Proverbs 18:9 (New Living Translation)

Christian Soldiers

In the 2nd Book of Timothy, Paul the Apostle encourages and challenges Timothy to be a soldier of Christ. What are the qualities of a good soldier? A good soldier needs to be prepared to fight the enemy. A soldier must be loyal, faithful, bold, courageous, and endure hardships. A soldier needs to be strong in body, mind, and spirit to engage in warfare. He needs to be quick, ready to take action on a moment's notice, and never give up until the mission is accomplished.

Are you a Christian soldier? Are you ready to take action to fight the evil of this world? You must keep your body, mind, and spirit prepared for battle. I'm not talking about a battle of bombs and gunfire but a spiritual battle. A battle of righteousness, faith, love, and peace. Our world is overrun by evil and the battle is constant. Will you stand up and win the war for God?

Formula for Success

I want to share with you a formula for success. Success is defined as achieving a favorable or desired outcome. This formula will work for any situation. It will work to produce the results you desire.

Attitude + Knowledge + Activity + Perseverance = Desired Results

Your attitude determines your motive and level of commitment to achieve your desired results. If you feel that your desired results is worth accomplishing and you think that you can achieve it and you visualize yourself achieving it, you can achieve your desired results. If you believe that God wants you to be healthy and you believe good health is worth accomplishing and you think that you can become healthy and you visualize yourself being healthy, you are a step closer to making good health a reality.

Knowledge is the clear perception of truth, it's a range of information, it's the understanding gained by personal experience and other's experience. If you want to achieve your desired results, you need to understand how to go about getting your desired results. You need information, understanding, and truth.

Have you ever heard the clichés "What you don't know won't hurt you" or "Ignorance is bliss?" Let me tell you that what you don't know *will* hurt you and ignorance is *not* bliss. Ignorance is poverty; ignorance is disaster. Educating yourself is a lifelong process.

You may have also heard the cliché "Knowledge is power." This is not true. Putting knowledge into action is power. Knowledge without activity is wasted. Your desired results will never be achieved if you don't take appropriate action.

Sometimes we don't achieve our desired results on our first try. If you don't succeed at first, try, try again! This is the concept of perseverance. Never give up until you've achieved your desired results. If you will put your plan into action, you will always get results. Sometimes you get your desired results, sometimes you get different results. If you don't arrive at your desired results, analyze your attitude, knowledge, and activity. Make adjustments, and try it again. It took Thomas Edison 2,001 attempts to create the light bulb. What would have happened if he gave up after 2,000 attempts?

Let me share with you the history of another man. This man

Failed at business at age 21.
Was defeated in a legislative race at age 22.
Failed again in business at age 24.
Overcame the death of his sweetheart at age 26.
Had a nervous breakdown at age 27.
Lost a congressional race at age 34.
Lost a congressional race at age 36.
Lost a senatorial race at age 45.
Failed in an effort to become vice-president at age 47.
Lost a senatorial race at age 49.
Was elected president of the United States at age 52.

The man's name was Abraham Lincoln. How might the history

of the United States be different if Abraham Lincoln did not persevere and keep trying?

God wants you to persevere and never give up on achieving His will for your life. He knows how difficult it is to keep trying. Sometimes it seems that you'll never achieve His will, but keep trying. God will reward you at the appropriate time.

> "Because you have obeyed my command to persevere, I will protect you from the great time of testing that will come upon the whole world to test those who belong to this world.
> **Revelation 3:10 (New Living Translation)**

Formula for Disaster

I shared with you a formula for success. Now let me share with you a formula for disaster.

Could → Should → Don't = Disaster

You know that you could be healthy by following God's way. You know that you should be healthy, God desires it for you. Yet, you don't apply God's simple principles and take action to be healthy. This scenario will always lead to disaster. Very often there are actions you could and should take in your life, yet for some reason you don't. Scripture tells us that if you know you should do something, and don't, you've committed a sin. Don't let sin destroy your life. Anything you could and should do in your life can be accomplished if you put your faith in the Lord and obey His will.

> Anyone, then, who knows the good he ought to do and doesn't do it, sins.
> **James 4:17 (New International Version, NIV)**

> The LORD has brought against us the disaster he prepared, for we did not obey him, and the LORD our God is just in everything he does.
> **Daniel 9:14 (New Living Translation)**

You have dreams, desires, and goals that you would like fulfilled in your lifetime. God also has specific goals for your life. In order to achieve any dream, desire or goal you must put together a plan to achieve those goals. In order for the plan to work, it must be put into action. Simply plan the work, then work the plan!

Ask God for help in prioritizing your health goals and creating a plan for achieving them. It is God's desire that you become a strong Christian soldier and fight the battle for Him. Will you undergo the training to become strong in body, mind, and spirit to get prepared for the battle? Despite the evil plans of mankind, God's way will ultimately prevail and He will bless those who follow His way!

> Many are the plans in a man's heart, but it is the Lord's purpose that prevails.
> **Proverbs 19:21 (New International Version, NIV)**

CHAPTER 17

Follow-up

You found your starting point on the road to better health (analysis), you decided where you want to go (set goals), you decided how to get there by creating a plan, put it into action and achieved many of your goals. Congratulations! What's next? Now you need to stay there and maintain your health. You went through a lot of work to build good health. Don't stop and let your health slip back and decline.

Maintaining good health is a lifetime commitment for the glory of God. It takes effort to maintain good health. It also takes effort to maintain poor health. Which would you prefer? Good health is a journey not a destination. Maintaining your health is your responsibility while living in God's earthly kingdom.

Maintaining your health is easier than you think. You made several changes in your lifestyle to build your health. You threw out your old health defeating habits and formed new health building habits. Follow your new habits, make refinements as needed and you will maintain good health. Remember that good health is the result of the body, mind, and spirit working together. I pray that the building and strengthening of your personal relationship with God while experiencing your health building program will provide the motivation you need to be proactive in maintaining your health.

All of us could use a little extra motivation now and then to keep our body, mind and spirit in peak performance. The best advice I can give you to stay motivated is to focus on God's purpose and goals for your life. God will help you find a way to stay motivated and excited about serving Him. Remember that a strong body, mind, and spirit is necessary to do your very best work for God. And doesn't God deserve your very best?

Another way to keep you motivated is to try new things. People have different thresholds of boredom. Sometimes performing the same routine over and over gets boring. If this happens to you, change your routine. There are several different types of aerobic and strength training exercises that you can choose to keep your exercise sessions interesting and challenging. Maybe your diet has gotten boring. Try new foods or try preparing new and different dishes with your favorite foods. There are many good cookbooks available that focus on healthy eating. Don't let boredom be an excuse for letting your health back slide.

Try celebrating your victories to keep your motivation levels high. Plan to give yourself rewards as you achieve significant goals. Whether it's a mini-vacation, a shopping spree, or dinner and a movie, impending rewards can help keep you focused on achieving your goals. Words of advice, don't ever use rewards that have a negative impact on your health. For example, don't reward yourself by eating junk foods. That's like taking a step backwards after you've worked so hard to achieve your forward momentum. If rewards keep you motivated, use them and build them into your action plans.

Don't let worldly views and opinions cloud your judgement or sway your thinking. Much of what you hear and witness in the secular world is not pleasing to God nor is it worthy of His glory. The Bible warns us of false prophets that will spread lies and nonsense and lure people away from Godly living.

> And many false prophets will appear and will lead many people astray.
> **Matthew 24:11 (New Living Translation)**

Living a sinful life is easy. The gate of lusts and worldly pleasures stands wide open. Many will find the pleasures of the world too attractive to pass up, but it leads to pain and destruction. On the other hand, living a Godly life is difficult because it is unpleasant to the flesh. The grace of God leads to peace and eternal life, yet few will find it.

> "Enter by the narrow gate; for wide is the gate and broad is the way that leads to destruction, and there are many who go in by it. Because narrow is the gate and difficult is the way which leads to life, and there

are few who find it.
Matthew 7:13-14 (New King James Version)

Satan will continuously try to lure you away from God through lies, deceit, and worldly pleasures. Stay the course, be strong in body, mind, and spirit. You belong to God. You are special. He will provide the guidance and strength to win the battle. Focus on Godly principles.

> But you belong to God, my dear children. You have already won your fight with these false prophets, because the Spirit who lives in you is greater than the spirit who lives in the world.
> **1 John 4:4 (New Living Translation)**

Guidelines for Maintaining Good Health

1. Stay focused on God's goals for your life.
2. Continue doing the things that brought you to good health.
3. Celebrate your victories.
4. Understand that God holds you accountable for maintaining your health.
5. Challenge yourself to be a Christian soldier. Stay prepared to fight the battles of evil.
6. Fellowship with people that are supporting, encouraging, and share similar values.
7. Don't be misled by worldly views and opinions.
8. If your routines get boring, making changes; try something new.
9. Challenge yourself; set goals that make you stretch your abilities.
10. Praise God and continue to draw strength from Him.

Table 17-1

Now it is your turn to set a good example for other people to follow. Go tell the world. Share your testimony with others who are in poor health, be it body, mind or spirit, and encourage them to follow God's road to good health and eternal life just like you did. Teach them how to find the love, grace, and abundant life that only God can provide.

> May the grace of our Lord Jesus Christ, the love of God, and the fellowship of the Holy Spirit be with you all.
> **2 Corinthians 13:13 (New Living Translation)**

Conclusion

The journey to good health, the Godly way, is a long and winding road that never seems to end. It truly does not end until you have completed your earthly mission and He calls you home to dwell with Him in heaven. That will be a glorious day! But until that time comes, it is imperative that you work to fulfill God's purpose for your life. The quality of your overall health, body, mind, and spirit determines your preparedness for achieving your particular mission. Be the best that you can be for the glory of God.

If you have come this far in this book and not yet taken action to become the Christian soldier that God wants you to be, I'm praying that you will take action today. Don't let pride and ego get in your way. Don't let these weaknesses keep you in bondage. Too often I see men let pride and ego hold them back from experiencing God's grace and abundant life. Too often I see men suffer the pain of the world instead of the peace of God. No matter what your current circumstances, there is hope in God. It doesn't matter whether you are the richest or the poorest, the weakest or the strongest: God can transform your life into something special. Give Him the opportunity to work in your life!

> Don't copy the behavior and customs of this world, but let God transform you into a new person by changing the way you think. Then you will know what God wants you to do, and you will know how good and pleasing and perfect his will really is.
> **Romans 12:2 (New Living Translation)**

The world is in dire need of Godly role models. Will you stand up and meet the challenge? Spouses, parents, pastors, teachers, corporate and community leaders; we need role models from all walks of life that will demonstrate righteous living not by word, but through your actions. Americans are weak in body, mind, and spirit.

Will you stand up and lead the lost sheep of God down the path to health, happiness, and prosperity as God would have it? I pray that you will act now to stop the moral and physical decline of America. The founding fathers of this nation fought hard and many gave their lives to establish a country based on Godly values. The early pioneers of this country endured many battles and hardships to insure the "American Dream" for future generations. An environment where families could flourish, live in peace, and worship God as they choose. As we begin the twenty-first century this is but a dream for some Americans and a reality that is quickly slipping away from the rest of America. Will you stand up for America, for the founding fathers, and for the past families that made America the greatest nation in the history of the world? It's not too late, this country can still be restored to greatness if you act now! You can make a difference. Will you be a role model that will strengthen your body, mind, and spirit and help others to do the same. Stand up for God. Stand up for the American people. God will provide strength and guidance to all who stand up for Him.

> I can do all things through Christ who strengthens me.
> **Philippians 4:13 (New King James Version)**

In closing, I want to leave you with a story about a little boy named Timmy that I received through email. The author is unknown.

Little Timmy's Whipping

There was a school with a class of students no teacher had been able to handle. The unruly students had run off two or three teachers from this school in one year. A young man, just out of college, heard about the class and he applied to the school. The principal asked the young man, "Do you not know what you are asking for? No one has been able to handle these students. You are just asking for a terrible beating." After a few moments of silent prayer, the young man looked at the principal and said, "Sir, with your consent I accept the challenge. Just give me a trial basis."

The next morning the young man stood before the class. He said to the class, "Young people, I came here today to conduct school. But I realize I can't do it by myself. I must have your help." One big boy, they called Big Tom, in the back of the room whispered to his buddies, "I'll not need any help. I can lick that little bird all by myself." The young teacher told the class that if they were to have school, there would have to be some rules to go by. But he also added that he would allow the students to make up the rules, that he would list them on the blackboard. This was certainly different, the students thought! One young man suggested "NO STEALING." Another one shouted, "BE ON TIME FOR CLASS." Pretty soon they had 10 rules listed on the board. The teacher had then asked the class what the punishment should be for breaking these rules. "Rules are no good unless they are enforced," he said. Someone in the class suggested that if the rules were broken, they should receive 10 licks with a rod across their back with their coat off. The teacher thought that this punishment was rather harsh, so he asked the class if they would stand by this punishment. The class agreed. Everything went pretty good for two or three days.

Then Big Tom came in one day very upset. He declared that someone had stolen his lunch. After talking with the students, they came to the conclusion that little Timmy had stolen Big Tom's lunch. Someone had seen little Timmy with Big Tom's lunch! The teacher called little Timmy up to the front of the room. Little Timmy admitted he had taken Big Tom's lunch. So the teacher asked him, "Do you know the punishment? Little Timmy nodded that he did. You must remove your coat, then," the teacher instructed. The little fellow had come with a great big coat on. Little Timmy said to the teacher, "I am guilty and I am willing to take my punishment, but please don't make me take off my coat." The teacher reminded little Timmy of the rules and punishments and again told him he must remove his coat and take his punishment like a man. The little fellow started to unbutton that old coat. As he did so, the teacher saw he did not have a shirt on under the coat. And even worse, he saw a frail and bony frame hidden beneath that coat. The teacher asked little Timmy why he had come to school without a shirt on. Little Timmy replied, "My daddy's dead and my mother is very poor. I don't have but one shirt, and my mother is washing it today. I wore big brother's coat to keep warm." That young teacher stood and looked at the frail back the ribs sticking out, the spine protruding against the skin. He wondered how he could lay a rod on that little back and without even a shirt on. Still, he knew he must enforce the punishment or the children would not obey the rules. So he drew back to strike little Timmy. Just then Big Tom stood up and came down the aisle. He asked, "Is there anything that says I can't take little Timmy's whipping for him?" The teacher thought about it and agreed. With that Big Tom ripped his coat off and stooped and stood over Little Timmy at the desk. Hesitatingly the teacher began to lay the rod on that big back. But for some strange reason, after only five licks that old rod just broke in half. The young teacher buried his face in his hands and began to sob. He heard a commotion and looked up to find not even one dry eye in the room. Little Timmy had turned and grabbed Big Tom around the neck, apologizing to him for stealing his lunch, begging his forgiveness. Little Timmy begged Big Tom to forgive him. He told Big Tom that he would love him till the day he died for taking his whipping for him.

Aren't you glad that Jesus took our whipping for us, that He shed His precious blood on Calvary so that you and I can have eternal life in Glory with Him? We are unworthy of the price He paid for us, but aren't you glad He loves us that much? This is a story everyone needs to hear. God loves us so much that he has provided everything we need for health, happiness, peace, prosperity, and eternal life. What more could anybody ask for? All we have to do is honor and obey Him.

God wants so badly to bestow His blessings upon you. God loves you so much that He gives you a choice. You have the choice of following His way or the ways of the world. You can follow God's way and know His love, peace, health, happiness, prosperity and eternal life or you can follow the worldly ways which leads to hate, anger, disease, emptiness, loneliness, and eternal separation from God. Which do you choose?

I pray that you will take the principles of this book and apply them to your life. Nobody has ever regretted following God's way. May God bless you!

APPENDICES

Appendix A - Essential Vitamins

Vitamin A

Functions: Builds immune system, develops strong bone cells, promotes healthy skin, hair, teeth and gums, counteracts weak eyesight and night blindness, reduces risk of cancer.

Symptoms of Deficiency: Acne, birth defects, chronic diarrhea, dry hair, eye dryness, fatigue, growth retardation, hair loss (baldness), infections, infertility, insomnia, loss of smell, night blindness, rough, itchy skin, weight loss.

Symptoms of Toxicity: Abdominal pain, hair loss (baldness), irritability, joint pain, loss of menstrual period, nausea and vomiting, upset intestinal tract, weight loss.

Daily Requirement: 15,000 IU

Food Sources: Apricots, asparagus, beet greens, broccoli, cantaloupe, carrots, collards, dandelion greens, dulse, eggs, fish liver and fish liver oil, garlic, kale, mustard greens, papayas, peaches, pumpkin, red peppers, spirulina, spinach, sweet potatoes, Swiss chard, turnip greens, watercress, and yellow squash.

Vitamin B1 (Thiamine)

Functions: Enhances circulation, assists in blood formation, carbohydrate metabolism and the production of hydrochloric acid, promotes brain function and activity, supports the nervous

	system and enhances the immune system.
Symptoms of Deficiency:	Anorexia, constipation, forgetfulness, gastrointestinal disturbances, coordination impairment, nervousness, edema, fatigue, irritability, numbness of the hands and feet, muscle atrophy, labored breathing, gastrointestinal disturbances, insomnia, depression, general weakness, and weight loss.
Symptoms of Toxicity:	None
Daily Requirement:	50 mg
Food Sources:	Brown rice, egg yolks, fish, whole grains, asparagus, broccoli, most nuts, oatmeal, brewer's yeast, peas, poultry, kelp, and Brussels sprouts.

Vitamin B2 (Riboflavin)

Functions:	Necessary for red blood cell formation, antibody production, energy production, fat, carbohydrate, and protein metabolism, and growth. Promotes healthy skin and vision, and helps prevent cataracts.
Symptoms of Deficiency:	Hair loss, blurred vision, cataracts, depression, dermatitis, eye disorders, insomnia, dizziness, growth retardation, light sensitivity, and poor digestion.
Symptoms of Toxicity:	None
Daily Requirement:	50 mg
Food Sources:	Meat, milk, whole grains, cheese, egg yolks, poultry, asparagus, brewer's yeast, broccoli, spinach, dandelion greens, kelp, green leafy vegetables, nuts, mushrooms, and Brussels sprouts.

Vitamin B3 (Niacin)

Functions:	Necessary for proper circulation, healthy skin and nervous system, energy production, cholesterol metabolism, synthesis of sex hormones, carbohydrate, fat, and protein metabolism and the production of hydrochloric acid for digestion.
Symptoms of Deficiency:	Anorexia, nausea, indigestion, mental illness, insomnia, bad breath, diarrhea, dermatitis, memory loss, dizziness, headache, irritability, fatigue, muscular weakness, limb pains, and skin eruptions.
Symptoms of Toxicity:	Niacin "flush" and liver impairment.
Daily Requirement:	100 mg
Food Sources:	Eggs, fish, milk, cheese, broccoli, carrots, tomatoes, brewer's yeast, potatoes, dandelion greens, and whole wheat products.

Vitamin B5 (Pantothenic Acid)

Functions:	Defends against stress, fatigue and nerve disorders, helps convert fats, carbohydrates, and proteins into energy, involved in the production of neurotransmitters and adrenal hormones.
Symptoms of Deficiency:	Fatigue, headache, muscle spasms, insomnia, depression, tingling in the hands, nausea and vomiting, and eczema.
Symptoms of Toxicity:	None
Daily Requirement:	100 mg
Food Sources:	Brown rice, poultry, brewer's yeast, broccoli, whole grains, yams, beef, eggs, and legumes.

Vitamin B6 (Pyridoxine)

Functions:	Promotes red blood cell formation, maintains sodium and potassium balance, carbohydrate, fat, and protein metabolism, production of hydrochloric acid, strengthens immunity system, cell reproduction, enhances enzyme activity, and anti-aging factor.
Symptoms of Deficiency:	Acne, hair loss, anemia, anorexia, nausea, arthritis, depression, dizziness, headache, fatigue, irritability, learning difficulties, hearing problems, oily facial skin, stunted growth, nervousness, water retention, seizures, weak memory, general weakness, and possibly carpal tunnel syndrome.
Symptoms of Toxicity:	Tingling of the skin.
Daily Requirement:	50 mg
Food Sources:	Bananas, brewer's yeast, buckwheat, carrots, chicken, meats, peas, spinach, fish, cantaloupe, cabbage, brown rice, broccoli, sunflower seeds, beans, avocado, and walnuts.

Vitamin B12 (Cobalamin)

Functions:	Red blood cell formation, prevents anemia, digestion and absorption of food, synthesis of protein, metabolism of fats and carbohydrates, cellular formation and longevity, energy production, and prevent nerve damage.
Symptoms of Deficiency:	Anemia, Depression, constipation, dizziness, headache, irritability, moodiness, fatigue, nervous system degeneration, unhealthy weight loss, and birth defects.
Symptoms of Toxicity:	None
Daily Requirement:	50 mg

Food Sources: Eggs, brewer's yeast, fish, milk, dairy products, kelp, and soybeans.

Vitamin C

Functions: Necessary for tissue growth and repair, strengthens immunity system, protects against cancer, heart disease, viral and bacterial infection and the harmful effects of pollution, aids in the production of anti-stress hormones, essential for the formation of collagen, protects against blood clotting and bruising, and promotes the healing of cuts and wounds.

Symptoms of Deficiency: Bleeding gums, easy bruising, irritability, joint pain, impaired wound healing, fatigue, poor digestion.

Symptoms of Toxicity: None

Daily Requirement: 2,000 mg

Food Sources: Citrus fruits (oranges, grapefruit, lemons), broccoli, cauliflower, green peppers, papaya, tomatoes, kiwi, asparagus, Brussel's sprouts, cantaloupe, collards, onions, turnip greens, spinach, green peas, dandelion greens, and mustard greens.

Vitamin D

Functions: Necessary for growth and development of bones, required for the absorption and utilization of calcium and phosphorus, needed in blood clotting, thyroid function, and muscle function.

Symptoms of Deficiency: Insomnia, diarrhea, nearsightedness, insomnia, nosebleeds, muscle cramps, slow healing, fast heartbeat, rickets in children and osteomalacia in adults, weight loss, and nervousness.

Symptoms of Toxicity: Arteriosclerosis and liver dysfunction.

Daily Requirement: 400 IU

Food Sources: Fish, dairy products, eggs, oatmeal, sweet potatoes, dandelion greens, and fish liver oils.

Vitamin E

Functions: An important antioxidant and immune stimulant, improves circulation, promotes normal blood clotting and healing, reduces blood pressure, enhances athletic performance, reduces leg cramps, retard cellular and mental aging, alleviates fatigue, and provides oxygen to body tissues.

Symptoms of Deficiency: Muscle and nerve degeneration, hair loss, dermatitis, infertility, anemia, miscarriage, uterine deterioration, heart disease, and cancer.

Symptoms of Toxicity: None

Daily Requirement: 400 IU

Food Sources: Whole grains, brown rice, eggs, kelp, dark green leafy vegetables, cold pressed vegetables oils, nuts, oatmeal, sweet potatoes, and wheat germ.

Vitamin K

Functions: Necessary for blood clotting, bone formation and repair

Symptoms of Deficiency: Poor blood clotting, internal bleeding, and osteoporosis.

Symptoms of Toxicity: Can cause flushing and sweating.

Daily Requirement: 140 mcg

Food Sources: Asparagus, broccoli, Brussel's sprouts, cabbage, oatmeal, soybeans, whole wheat, dark green leafy vegetables, eggs, and cauliflower.

Biotin

Functions: Metabolism of carbohydrates, fats, and proteins, cell growth, and promotes healthy hair and skin

Symptoms of Deficiency: Hair loss, anemia, fatigue, muscle pain and weakness, insomnia, depression, anorexia, nausea, skin disorders, high blood sugar, and soreness of the tongue.

Symptoms of Toxicity: None

Daily Requirement: 300 mcg

Food Sources: Poultry, brewer's yeast, raspberries, grapefruit, tomatoes, saltwater fish, eggs, meat, and milk.

Choline

Functions: Brain nutrient and neurotransmitter, fat and cholesterol metabolism.

Symptoms of Deficiency: Inability to digest fats, high blood pressure, impaired brain function and memory, impaired kidney and liver function.

Symptoms of Toxicity: None

Daily Requirement: 200 mg

Food Sources: Eggs, fish, meat, milk, soybeans, and whole grain cereals.

Bioflavinoids

Functions: Prevent arteries from hardening, enhance blood

	vessel, capillary, and vein strength, protects connective tissue, controls bruising, internal bleeding, and mouth herpes, prevents cataracts, lowers cholesterol, promotes circulation, protects against bacterial infection, and stimulates bile production.
Symptoms of Deficiency:	Easy bruising and bleeding, potential for connective tissue injuries.
Symptoms of Toxicity:	Diarrhea
Daily Requirement:	500 mg
Food Sources:	Apricots, cherries, grapefruit, grapes, lemons, oranges, peppers, buckwheat, and black currents.

Folic Acid

Functions:	Essential for division and growth of cells, synthesis of DNA and RNA, enzyme efficiency, blood formation, energy production, strengthens immunity, and protein metabolism.
Symptoms of Deficiency:	Anemia, anorexia, apathy, birth defects, fatigue, growth retardation, headache, insomnia, memory loss, and digestive disturbances.
Symptoms of Toxicity:	None
Daily Requirement:	400 mcg
Food Sources:	Broccoli, brewer's yeast, soybeans, peas, green leafy vegetables, barley, beef, legumes, lentils, chicken, brown rice, wheat germ, whole grains, oranges, salmon, and tuna.

Inositol

Functions:	Protects against male pattern baldness, high blood pressure, and arteriosclerosis, enhances

	oxygen delivery to body tissues, lowers cholesterol, and fat metabolism.
Symptoms of Deficiency:	Arteriosclerosis, constipation, eczema, high cholesterol, irritability, and mood swings.
Symptoms of Toxicity:	None
Daily Requirement:	100 mg
Food Sources:	Beans, onions, oranges, peanut butter, oats, peas, tomatoes, zucchini, brewer's yeast, meat, milk, and whole grains.

Appendix B - Essential Minerals

Boron

Functions: Enhances calcium, magnesium, phosphorus, and vitamin D use in bone formation, stimulates estrogen and testosterone production, prevents against bone loss.

Symptoms of Deficiency: Osteoporosis, hot flashes and vaginal dryness in post-menopausal symptoms.

Symptoms of Toxicity: None

Daily Requirement: 2 mg

Food Sources: Apples, carrots, grapes, leafy vegetables, nuts, pears, and grains.

Calcium

Functions: Most abundant mineral in the body. Essential for bone and teeth formation and the maintenance of healthy gums, regulates heartbeat and cell division, transmits nerve impulses, cell membrane regulation, regulation of insulin secretion, muscular growth and contraction, lowers cholesterol, lowers blood pressure, blood clotting, and prevent cardiovascular disease.

Symptoms of Deficiency: Arthritis, bone spurs, brittle fingernails, depression, eczema, high blood pressure, high cholesterol, hyperactivity, insomnia, irritability, muscle cramps, nervousness, osteoporosis, kidney stones, low back pain, periodontal disease, retarded

	growth, and tooth decay.
Symptoms of Toxicity:	Anorexia, depression, irritability, memory loss, muscle weakness, heart arrhythmias, growth retardation, high blood pressure, constipation, kidney disease, and liver impairment
Daily Requirement:	1,500 mg
Food Sources:	Milk and dairy foods, green leafy vegetables, brewer's yeast, egg yolks, asparagus, broccoli, mustard greens, collard greens, mustard greens, kale, almonds, kelp, cabbage, and oats.

Chromium

Functions:	Essential for glucose tolerance and sugar regulation, synthesis of cholesterol, fats, and proteins.
Symptoms of Deficiency:	High cholesterol, diabetes or hypoglycemia, premature aging, anxiety, and fatigue.
Symptoms of Toxicity:	Dermatitis, gastrointestinal ulcers, kidney dysfunction, and liver impairment
Daily Requirement:	150 mcg
Food Sources:	Brewer's yeast, honey, whole grains, cheese, grapes, raisins, brown rice, meat, chicken, eggs, and potatoes.

Copper

Functions:	Energy production, healing process, hair and skin coloring, taste sensitivity, formation of bone, hemoglobin, red blood cells, and elastin, healthy nerves and joints.
Symptoms of Deficiency:	High cholesterol, osteoporosis, anemia, heart arrhythmias, hair loss, diarrhea, depression, learning disabilities, loss of hair color, aneurysms, and fatigue.
Symptoms	Depression, irritability, joint pain, muscle pain,

of Toxicity:	nervousness, nausea, and vomiting.
Daily Requirement:	3 mg
Food Sources:	Eggs, legumes, soybeans, green leafy vegetables, oranges, pecans, almonds, broccoli, garlic, mushrooms, oats, and raisins.

Germanium

Functions:	Improves cellular oxygenation keeping the immune system strong.
Symptoms of Deficiency:	Impaired immune system, arthritis, osteoporosis, low energy, and cancer.
Symptoms of Toxicity:	None
Daily Requirement:	30 mg
Food Sources:	Chlorella, garlic, tuna, reishi mushrooms, aloe vera, ginseng, onions, shiitake mushrooms, and leafy greens.

Iodine

Functions:	Essential for good thyroid function and proper metabolism, helps metabolize excess fat and is important for physical and mental development.
Symptoms of Deficiency:	Goiter, hypothyroidism, cretinism, confused thinking, menstrual difficulties, weight gain, and fatigue
Symptoms of Toxicity:	Metallic taste and sores in the mouth, swollen salivary glands, diarrhea, and vomiting.
Daily Requirement:	225 mcg
Food Sources:	Saltwater fish, kelp, asparagus, garlic, lima beans, mushrooms, soybeans, spinach, summer squash, Swiss chard, and turnip greens.

Iron

Functions:	Essential ingredient in the production of hemoglobin and oxygenation of the red blood cells. Important for growth, enzyme activity, healthy immune system, and energy production.
Symptoms of Deficiency:	Anemia, fatigue, muscle weakness, anorexia, brittle nails confusion, dizziness, constipation, headaches, obesity, irritability, growth retardation, and digestive disturbances.
Symptoms of Toxicity:	Anorexia, dizziness, fatigue, and headaches.
Daily Requirement:	18 mg
Food Sources:	Eggs, fish, whole grains, cherries, leafy greens, poultry, legumes, meat, almond's, brewer's yeast, kelp, kidney and lima beans, lentils, raisins, rice, and soybeans.

Lithium

Functions:	Important for psychological stability and behavior.
Symptoms of Deficiency:	Depression, bi-polar disease, hyperactivity, ADD, ADHD, aggressiveness, and violent behavior.
Symptoms of Toxicity:	Heart palpitations, nausea, vomiting, confusion, drowsiness, weight gain, excessive urination, and headaches.
Daily Requirement:	650 mcg to 2 mg
Food Sources:	Whole grains and seeds. Small amounts are found in a wide variety of foods.

Magnesium

Functions:	Necessary for good nerve and muscle function, healthy blood vessels and blood pressure, prevents calcification of soft tissues, vital for enzyme activity, and helps maintain body pH

balance.

Symptoms of Deficiency: Irritability, nervousness, anxiety, restlessness, depression, birth defects, calcification of soft tissues, dizziness, poor digestion, diabetes, hyperactivity, insomnia, muscle weakness, seizures, and heart palpitations.

Symptoms of Toxicity: None

Daily Requirement: 750 mg

Food Sources: Dark green vegetables, fish, meat, whole grains, dairy products, nuts, legumes, apples, apricots, bananas, brewer's yeast, brown rice, cantaloupe, garlic, grapefruit, kelp, lemons, lima beans, peaches, and soybeans.

Manganese

Functions: Nourishes the brain and nerves. Necessary for DNA/RNA production, protein and fat metabolism, energy production, blood sugar regulation, bone growth, joint health, and a healthy immune system.

Symptoms of Deficiency: Atherosclerosis, dizziness, hearing loss, high cholesterol, hypoglycemia, hypertension, irritability, memory loss, excessive perspiration, rapid pulse, pancreatic damage, repetitive motion syndrome, and confusion.

Symptoms of Toxicity: Anorexia, impaired judgement, memory loss, and interference with iron absorption.

Daily Requirement: 5 mg

Food Sources: Avocados, seaweed, whole grains, nuts, eggs, green leafy vegetables, legumes, pineapple, bananas, and blueberries.

Molybdenum

Functions: Promotes normal cell function and a component of certain metabolic enzymes.

Symptoms of Deficiency: Mouth and gum disorders, cancer, and impotence in older males

Symptoms of Toxicity: Gout-like disease and interference with copper metabolism.

Daily Requirement: 250 mcg

Food Sources: Whole grains, brown rice, brewer's yeast, legumes, peas, and dark green leafy vegetables.

Phosphorus

Functions: Bone and tooth formation, cell growth, maintains acid-alkaline balance, kidney function, and contraction of the heart muscle.

Symptoms of Deficiency: Anxiety, anorexia, bone pain, fatigue, irritability, numbness, weight loss, trembling, irregular breathing, and weakness.

Symptoms of Toxicity: Calcium malabsorption, loose teeth, osteoporosis, tooth loss, and weight loss.

Daily Requirement: 1,000 – 1,500 mg

Food Sources: Eggs, fish, poultry, dairy products, nuts, legumes, asparagus, brewer's yeast, garlic, sesame, sunflower, and pumpkin seeds, bran, and whole grains.

Potassium

Functions: Transmits electrical signals between cells and nerves, enhances athletic performance, maintains acid-alkaline balance; necessary for muscle function, energy storage, nerve stability, enzyme and hormone production; works with sodium to control water balance, and helps maintain stable blood pressure.

Symptoms of Deficiency: Acne, arrhythmia, constipation, depression water retention, fatigue, growth retardation, high cholesterol, low blood pressure, insomnia, muscle weakness, nervousness, rapid heart rate, dry skin, insatiable thirst, salt retention, nausea, vomiting, and chills.

Symptoms of Toxicity: Cardiac arrest, difficulty in articulating words due to disease of the central nervous system, loss of or deficiency in the power to use or understand language as a result of injury to or disease of the brain, and weakness.

Daily Requirement: 2,000 mg

Food Sources: Poultry, fish, dairy foods, legumes, fruit, meat, vegetables, whole grains, apricots, avocados, bananas, brewer's yeast, brown rice, garlic, nuts, potatoes, winter squash, and yams.

Selenium

Functions: Protects the body from free radical damage and heavy metal toxicity, works with vitamin E to prevent fat and cholesterol accumulation in the bloodstream, protects against tumor formation, protects the heart against weakness and degeneration, enhances elasticity of skin and body tissue.

Symptoms of Deficiency: Aging skin, cancer, heart disease, cystic fibrosis, exhaustion, growth impairment, high cholesterol, impaired immunity, sterility, liver impairment, and cataracts.

Symptoms of Toxicity: Arthritis, hair loss, brittle nails, garlic breath, kidney and liver dysfunction.

Daily Requirement: 200 mcg

Food Sources: Brewer's yeast, eggs, sesame seeds, cabbage, garlic, tuna, meats, onions, kelp, fish, turnips, and brussels sprouts.

Silicon

Functions: Necessary for the health and growth of connective tissue, collagen production, healthy skin, nails, and hair; stimulates the immune system and prevents cardiovascular disease.

Symptoms of Deficiency: Dry brittle finger and toenails, poor skin quality, poor calcium utilization, and artery disease.

Symptoms of Toxicity: None

Daily Requirement: 200 - 500 mg

Food Sources: Whole grains, alfalfa, beets, brown rice, bell peppers, soybeans, and leafy green vegetables.

Sodium

Functions: Necessary for maintaining proper water balance and blood pH; necessary for stomach, nerve, and muscle function.

Symptoms of Deficiency: Abdominal cramps, anorexia, confusion, fatigue, headache, depression, flatulence, low blood pressure, memory loss, muscle weakness, nausea and vomiting, taste loss, and weight loss.

Symptoms of Toxicity: Water retention, high blood pressure, kidney disease, anorexia, irritability, weight gain, and congestive heart failure.

Daily Requirement: 2,400 mg

Food Sources: Celery, sauerkraut, olives, beets, cheese; virtually all foods have some sodium.

Sulphur

Functions: Necessary for smooth skin, glossy hair, hard nails, and collagen synthesis; critical for protein absorption, stimulates bile production, and

	protects against toxic substances.
Symptoms of Deficiency:	Arthritis, weakened ligaments and tendons, joint pain, Systemic Lupus Erythematosis, irritability, sickle cell anemia, and collagen diseases.
Symptoms of Toxicity:	Anemia, impaired digestion, and skin rashes.
Daily Requirement:	Unknown
Food Sources:	Eggs, fish, onions, garlic, hot peppers, brussels sprouts, cabbage, meats, turnips, and soybeans.

Vanadium

Functions:	Necessary for cell metabolism, formation of bones and teeth, growth and reproduction, and inhibits cholesterol synthesis.
Symptoms of Deficiency:	Heart disease, infertility, high cholesterol, slow growth, obesity, depression, ADD, ADHD, infant mortality, diabetes, and hypoglycemia.
Symptoms of Toxicity:	Unknown
Daily Requirement:	Unknown
Food Sources:	Dill, whole grains, meat, fish, olives, vegetable oils, snap beans, and radishes.

Zinc

Functions:	Essential for the formation of insulin, required for protein synthesis and collagen formation, necessary for strong immunity, helps prevent birth defects, production of digestive enzymes, enhances sensory perception, promotes mental alertness, and accelerates healing.
Symptoms of Deficiency:	Loss of taste and smell, thin fingernails with white spots that easily peel, acne, fatigue, growth impairment, nervousness, arteriosclero-

	sis, diabetes, hypoglycemia, high cholesterol, hair loss, anorexia, birth defects, depression, eczema, irritability, memory loss, apathy, impotence, impaired night vision, prostrate problems, infertility, slow wound healing, and increased susceptibility to infection.
Symptoms of Toxicity:	Iron deficiency, diarrhea, nausea, vomiting, mental depression
Daily Requirement:	30 mg
Food Sources:	Brewer's yeast, mushrooms, egg yolks, fish, kelp, lamb, legumes, lima beans, meats, pecans, poultry, soybeans, whole grains, and sunflower and pumpkin seeds,

Appendix C

Character Self-Assessment			
Read each sentence and score according to the rating scale below. Remember this is a character assessment. Answer honestly. **Rating Scale** This trait is characteristic of me: 1 – Very seldom 2 – Sometimes 3 – Usually 4 – Most of the time 5 – Almost always			
Trait		**Score**	
Honesty	• I'm truthful, sincere, and straightforward.		
	• I do not lie, cheat, or steal.		
	• I do not intentionally mislead others.		
Integrity	• I always do what is right, even when it is costly or difficult.		
	• I do not compromise my values by giving in to temptation.		
Reliability	• I follow through on commitments.		
	• I keep my promises.		
Respect	• I treat others the way I want to be treated.		
	• I have consideration for others.		
Responsibility	• I'm accountable for my actions; I don't make excuses or blame others.		

Appendix C

	• I do what needs to be done.	
	• I finish what I start.	
Fairness	• I treat people equally and impartially.	
	• I'm open minded and reasonable.	
	• I play by the rules.	
	• I do not take advantage of others.	
Caring	• I treat others with kindness, concern, and generosity.	
	• I'm charitable.	
	• I give of myself for the benefit of others.	
Citizenship	• I make our democratic republic work by voicing opinions, voting, and participating in the decision making process.	
	• I perform community service.	
	• I help take care of the environment.	
	• I obey the laws.	
	Total Score	

Scoring

92 – 115 You are a person of high character.

69 – 91 You are a person of good character, but there is room for improvement.

46 – 68 You are a person of little character. You need to make a sincere effort to improve your character.

23 – 45 If it weren't for bad character, you'd have no character at all. Seek help immediately!

Appendix D

Health Assessment Worksheet

Name: ______________________________ **Date:**

Body

Weight __________ Blood Pressure ______/______

Resting Heart Rate __________

Total Cholesterol __________

On the average I get ________ hours of sleep per night.

Please Check (√) All Conditions That Currently Apply To You:

☐ Acne	☐ Dry Skin	☐ Kidney Disease
☐ Allergies	☐ Edema (Water Retention)	☐ Low Energy
☐ Anxiety	☐ Frequent Infections/Colds	☐ Memory Loss
☐ Arthritis	☐ Gall Bladder	☐ Menopausal
☐ Asthma	☐ Gastritis	☐ Menstrual Cramps
☐ Cancer	☐ Heart Disease	☐ Muscle Cramps
☐ Coffee Drinker	☐ Hyperactivity	☐ PMS
☐ Constipation	☐ Hyperthyroid	☐ Pregnant
☐ Depression	☐ Hypoglycemia	☐ Prostrate Problems
☐ Diabetes	☐ Hypothyroid	☐ Smoker
☐ Diarrhea	☐ Insomnia	☐ Stress
☐ Digestive Problems	☐ Joint Pain	☐

Evaluation/Recommendation Notes

Current Medications: 1. __________ 2. __________ 3. __________ 4. __________

Fitness Components	**Assessment**	**Evaluation/Recommendation Notes**
Aerobic Endurance:		
Muscular Strength:		
Muscular Endurance:		
Flexibility:		

Appendix D

Health Assessment Worksheet

Body
(Cont.)

Body Composition: ____________ % Body Fat

Girth Measurements:

Neck ____________ Hips ____________

Arm ____________ (Halfway between shoulder and elbow)

Thigh ____________ (Halfway between hip and knee)

Chest ____________

Calf ____________ (Thickest part)

Waist ____________

Mind

Character Assessment Score: ____________

Attitude Assessment Score: ____________

Spirit

Spiritual Assessment Score: ____________

Evaluation/Recommendation Notes

References

Chapter 2

Advocates for Youth's Teen Pregnancy Prevention, www.advocatesforyouth.org/tpp.htm

Alaska Task Force on Parity for Mental Health, akmhcweb.org/parity/finalyrpt.htm

American Association of Suicidology, www.suicidology.org

American Cancer Association, www.cancer.org

American Heart Association, www.americanheart.org

Centers for Disease Control, www.cdc.gov

Central Illinois Right To Life, www.cirtl.org/stats.htm

Federal Bureau of Investigation Uniform Crime Report - 2000, www.fbi.gov/ucr/00cius.htm

Health Care Financing Administration, www.hcfa.gov/stats/NHE-Proj/proj1998/tables/table1a.htm

Healthy Kids.Com, www.healthykids.com

Midland County Friend of the Court, www.midlandcounty.org/foc/stat.htm

National Mental Health Association Fact Sheet, www.nmha.org/infoctr/factsheets/15.cfm

The Ugly Side of Alcohol, Dr. Allen Douma, Tribune Media Services,broadcast.webpoint.com/wpix/alcohol/alcohol_facts.htm

World Health Organization, *World Health Report 1999*, www.who.int/whr/1999.

Chapter 3

Guinness World Records 2000 – Millennium Edition

Wallach, Joel D. and Ma Lan. *Rare Earths, Forbidden Cures*. Bonita, CA: Double Happiness Publishing Co., 1996

Chapter 4

Jensen, Bernard and Mark Anderson. *Empty Harvest.* Garden City Park, NY: Avery Publishing Group, Inc., 1990.

Malkmus, George H. *Why Christians Get Sick.* Shippensburg, PA: Treasure House an Imprint of Destiny Image Publishers, Inc., 1998.

Chapters 5, 6, 7 and 8

Aihara, Herman. *Acid & Alkaline.* 5th Ed. Oroville, CA: George Ohsawa Macrobiotic Foundation, 1986.

Balch, James F. and Phyllis A. Balch. *Prescription For Nutritional Healing.* 2nd ed. Garden City Park, NY: Avery Publishing Group, 1997.

Ballentine, Rudolph. *Diet & Nutrition: A Holistic Approach.* Honesdale, PA: The Himalayan International Institute, 1978.

Barefoot, Robert R. and Carl J Reich. *The Calcium Factor.* Wickenburg, AZ: Deonna Enterprises Publishing, 1999.

Baroody, Theodore A. *Alkalize Or Die.* 5th Ed. Waynesville, NC: Holographic Health Press, 2000.

Batmanghelidj, F. *Your Body's Many Cries For Water.* 2nd ed. Falls Church, VA: Global Health Solutions, Inc., 2000.

Botkin, Daniel. *God's Dietary Laws: Abolished in the New Testament?*, www.giveshare.org/Health/dietarylaws.html, 2001.

Brown, Susan E. *Better Bones, Better Body.* New Canaan, CT: Keats Publishing, Inc., 1996.

Central Highlands Christian Publications. *Unclean Animals and Food Examined From a Biblical Perspective*, member. austasia.net/~barmstro/unclean.htm, 2001.

Clean and Unclean Creatures Based On Leviticus 11 and Deuteronomy 14, www.bibleresearch.org/lawbook4/b4w10.html, 2001.

Clean and Unclean Meats – Scriptural Proof Law of Unclean Still In Force, www.giveshare.org/Health/health5.html, 2001.

Columbia University College of P & S Complete Home Medical Guide, *Overview of Alcohol-Related Problems*, www.cpmcnet. columbia.edu/texts/guide/hmg06_0003.html.

Donsbach, Kurt W. *Nutrition in Action*. 1996.

Downing, Damien. *Daylight Robbery*. www.ddowning.demon.co.uk/daylight/daylight.html. 2001

Erasmus, Udo. *Fats That Heal, Fats That Kill*. 4th Printing. Burnaby, BC Canada: Alive Books, 1996.

Griffiths, Joel and Chris Bryson. "Flouride, Teeth, and The Atomic Bomb," www.nofluoride.com/a_bomb_&teeth.htm, 1997.

Holford, Patrick. *The Optimum Nutrition Bible*. Freedom, CA: The Crossing Press, 1999.

Jensen, Bernard and Mark Anderson. *Empty Harvest*. Garden City Park, NY: Avery Publishing Group, Inc., 1990.

Lankford, T. Randall. *Foundations of Normal and Therapeutic Nutrition*. Albany, NY: Delmar Publishers Inc., 1994.

Pitchford, Paul. *Healing With Whole Foods: Oriental Traditions and Modern Nutrition*. Berkeley, CA: North Atlantic Books, 1993.

Price, Weston A. *Nutrition and Physical Degeneration*. New Canaan, CT: Keats Publishing, Inc., 1989.

Rector-Page, Linda G. *Healthy Healing An Alternative Healing Reference*. 9th ed. Healthy Healing Publications, 1992.

Russel, Rex. W*hat The Bible Says About Healthy Living*. Ventura, CA: Regal Books, 1996.

Stitt, Paul A. *Beating The Food Giants*. Manitowoc, WI: Natural Press, 1993.

The Bitter Truth About Artificial Sweeteners, www.nexus-magazine.com//Aspartame.html.

Wallach, Joel D. and Ma Lan. *Dead Doctors Don't Lie*. Franklin, TN: Legacy Communications Group, 1999.

Wallach, Joel D. and Ma Lan. *Rare Earths, Forbidden Cures*. Bonita, CA: Double Happiness Publishing Co., 1996

Whiting, Steven E. *Self Health*. San Diego, CA: Institute of Nutritional Science, 1996.

Whitney, Eleanor Noss, Eva May Nunnelley Hamilton, and Sharon Rady Rolfes. *Understanding Nutrition*, 5th ed. St. Paul, MN: West Publishing Company, 1990.

Yiamouyiannis, John. *Fluoride The Aging Factor*. Delaware, OH: Health Action Press, 1993.

Chapter 9

American College of Sports Medicine. *ACSM'S Resource Manual For Guidelines For Exercise Testing And Prescription*, 2nd ed. Malvern, PA: Lea & Febiger, 1993.

American Heart Association. *Exercise Tips for Older Americans*, www.americanheart.org/Health/Lifestyle/Physical_Activity/Old Tips.html

American Heart Association. *Older Americans and Physical Activity Fact Sheet*, www.americanheart.org/Health/Lifestyle/Physical_Activity/OldFact.html

Cancer Research Foundation of America. *Men's Health – Exercise Tips*, www.preventcancer.org/mhexercise.cfm

Cancer Research Foundation of America. *Women's Health – Exercise Tips*, www.preventcancer.org/whexercise.cfm

Excuses, Excuses… Getting Started with an Exercise Program, www.healthchecksystems.com/excuses.htm

Exercise (Physical Activity), www.justmove.org/fitnessnews/hfbodyframe.cfm?Target=exercise.html

Exercise (Physical Activity) and Children, www.justmove.org/fitnessnews/hfbodyframe.cfm?Target=exerckids.html

McGlynn, George. *Dynamics of Fitness*, 2nd ed. Dubuque, IA: Wm. C. Brown Publishers, 1990.

Physical Activity and Cardiovascular Health: Fact Sheet, www.justmove.org/fitnessnews/hfbodyframe.cfm?Target=cardiofacts.html

The Benefits of Daily Physical Activity, www.justmove.org/fitnessnews/hfbodyframe.cfm?Target=dailybene.html

The Fitness Basics, www.chitrib.webpoint.com/fitness/fitbasic.htm

Chapter 10

Dement, William C. and Christopher Vaughan. *The Promise of Sleep*. New York, NY: Dell Publishing a division of Random House, Inc., 1999.

Encarta Encyclopedia. *Sleep*, www.encarta.msn.com/find/Concise.asp?ti=04C48000

HeliosHealth.com. *The Nature of Sleep*, www.helioshealth.com/sleep

How To Sleep Well, www.stanford.edu/~dement/howto.html

Loughborough Sleep Research Centre. *The Phenomena of Human Sleep*. The Karger Gazette – April 1997, www.lboro.ac.uk/departments/hu/groups/sleep/karger.htm

Mayo Clinic. *Sleep Well: 10 Tips for Better Sleep*, www.mayohealth.org/mayo/9910/htm/sleepwell.htm

Mylife.com. *Sleep Disorders*, www.mylifepath.com/topic/sleepdis

National Sleep Foundation. *2001 Sleep In America Poll*, www.sleepfoundation.org/publications/2001poll.html

National Center on Sleep Disorders Research Pamphlet, www.nhlbi.nih.gov/health/profs/sleep/sleep.txt

National Sleep Foundation. *Less Fun, Less Sleep, More Work – An American Portrait*, www.sleepfoundation.org/ PressArchives/lessfun_lesssleep.html

National Sleep Foundation. *2001 Sleep In America Poll*, www.sleepfoundation.org/publications/2001poll.html

Neurologychannel. *Sleep Disorders*, www.neurologychannel.com/sleepdisorders/

Sleepchannel. *Sleep Stages*, www.sleepdisorderchannel.com/stages/

Sleep To Live, www.sleepolive.com/sleep2live.htm

The Functions of Sleep, www.csmi.med.ed.ac.uk/session2/group11/functions.htm

Time for Kids World Report Edition. *But I'm Not Tired*, www.time-forkids.com/TFK/archive/000428/000428_sleep.html

U.S. News. *Today's Kids: Overscheduled and Overtired*, www.usnews.com/usnews/issue/001016/nycu/sleep.b.htm

Chapters 11 and 12

4MYCHILD. *About Cerebral Palsy*, www.cerebralpalsy.org

ALS Association, www.alsa.org

Alzheimer's Disease Education and Referral Center, www.alzheimers.org

American Brain Tumor Association, www.abta.org

American Parkinson Disease Association, www. apda parkinson.com

Awakenings. *Attitude*, www.lessons4living.com

Brainnet.Org. *Alzheimer's Disease*, www.brainnet.org/ alzheimers.

htm

Brainnet.Org. *Cerebral Palsy*, www.brainnet.org/cerebralpalsy.htm

Burns, Steven L. *The Medical Basis of Stress, Depression, Anxiety, Sleep Problems, and Drug Use.* www.teachhealth.com, 1990.

Character Counts. *The Six Pillars of Character*, www.character-counts.org/defsix.htm

Collinge, William. *Mind/Body Medicine: The Dance of Soma and Psyche.* www.healthy.net/asp/templates/article.asp?PageType=article&ID=1949.

Effective Stress Management, www.psychwww.com/mtsite/smund-str.html

Hart, Archibald D. *Adrenaline and Stress*, Dallas, TX: Word Publishing, 1995.

Josephson Institute of Ethics. *Making Ethical Decisions - The Six Pillars of Character*, www.josephsoninstitute.org/ MED/med6P.htm

Mark, Vernon H. and Jeffrey P. Mark. B*rain Power.* Boston, MA: Houghton Mifflin Company, 1989.

Mind/Body Medical Institute. *What is Mind/Body Medicine?*, www.mbmi.org/pages/mbb_mbm1.asp

MyNewAttitude.com. *How to Change Your Attitude Today!*, www.mynewattitude.com/article1010.html

National Multiple Sclerosis Society, www.nationalmssociety.org

National Parkinson Foundation, www.parkinson.org

ParenthoodWeb.com. *Children and TV Violence*, www.parenthood-web.com/parent_cfmfiles/pros.cfm?n=247

Pfeiffer, Carl C. *Nutrition and Mental Illness.* Rochester, VT: Healing Arts Press, 1987.

Robbins, Anthony. *Unlimited Power.* New York, NY: Ballantine Books, 1986.

Rinke, Wolf J. T*he 6 Success Strategies For Winning At Life, Love & Business*, Deerfield Beach, FL: Health Communications, Inc., 1996.

Robbins, Anthony. *Unlimited Power.* New York, NY: Ballantine Books, 1986.

Sahelian Ray. M*ind Boosters.* New York, NY: St. Martin's Press, 2000.

Stanley, Charles F. Success God's Way. Nashville, TN: Thomas Nelson Inc., 2000.

The American Institute of Stress. *Stress*, www.stress.org
The Huntington's Disease Society of America, www.hdsa.org
University of Washington. *Stress Management*, www.orthop.washington.edu/bonejoint/xzzztzzz1_2.html

Chapter 15

Stanley, Charles F. *Set Your Goals and Live By Faith.* Atlanta, GA: In Touch Ministries, 1980.
Stanley, Charles F. Success God's Way. Nashville, TN: Thomas Nelson Inc., 2000.

Chapter 16

Robbins, Anthony. *Unlimited Power.* New York, NY: Ballantine Books, 1986.
Rohn, Jim. *Take Charge of Your Life* (audiocassette series). Chicago, IL: Nightingale-Conant Corporation

Appendices A and B

Balch, James F. and Phyllis A. Balch. *Prescription For Nutritional Healing*. 2nd ed. Garden City Park, NY: Avery Publishing Group, 1997.
Holford, Patrick. *The Optimum Nutrition Bible*. Freedom, CA: The Crossing Press, 1999.
Rector-Page, Linda G. *Healthy Healing An Alternative Healing Reference.* 9th ed. Healthy Healing Publications, 1992.
Wallach, Joel D. and Ma Lan. *Dead Doctors Don't Lie*. Franklin, TN: Legacy Communications Group, 1999.
Wallach, Joel D. and Ma Lan. *Let's Play Doctor*. Bonita, CA: Double Happiness Publishing Co., 1989.
Wilson, Lawrence D. *Nutritional Balancing and Hair Mineral Analysis*. Prescott, AZ: L. D. Wilson Consultants, Inc., 1998.

Printed in the United States
736100004B